ANNUAL 1990

CONTENTS

All football facts correct at time of going to press.

ISBN: 1 85386 144 8

Published by Fleetway Publications, Greater London House, Hampstead Road, London NW1 7QQ. Maxwell Magazine Publishing Corporation Ltd. Sole agents for Australia and New Zealand: Gordon & Gotch Ltd. South Africa: Central News Agency. Reproduction by Moffat Reproductions Ltd., High Wycombe, Bucks, England. Printed and bound in Great Britain by BPCC Paulton Books Limited.

Roy of the Rovers

BUT IT WAS ROVERS' MID-FIELDER BLACKIE GRAY WHO TOOK THE BALL ON THE VOLLEY!
ROVERS
CUT OUT THAT CHIP!
YESSSS... GREAT GOAL!
ONE EACH! STILL ENOUGH TIME TO GRAB THE WINNER! KEEP AT 'EM, LADS!
BUT IT WAS HARTFORD UNITED WHO CAME STORMING UPFIELD IN A BREAKAWAY ATTACK!
ONE, TWO, THREE, FOUR! THEY'RE MOVING THROUGH US LIKE A KNIFE THROUGH BUTTER!
DON'T WORRY, BIG DUNC WILL STOP 'EM IN THEIR TRACKS!
GNNFF!
VETERAN SCOTTISH INTERNATIONAL LEFT-BACK DUNCAN McKAY WAS RENOWNED FOR HIS TOUGH TACKLING!
SOLID AS A ROCK, LIKE ALWAYS! MAKE GROUND, MAC!

BUT FROM OUT OF NOWHERE CAME A SECOND UNITED FORWARD...
GRAAAGH!
FOUL, REF!

N-NOT MUCH PAIN, ROY, BUT... I FEEL NUMB FROM THE WAIST UP!
YOU'VE PROBABLY TORN A BACK MUSCLE. I'M TAKING YOU OFF, MAC!

ONLY THREE MINUTES TO GO, ROY. WE CAN EASILY HANG ON AND EARN A DRAW... BUT DUNCAN'S INJURY WORRIES ME!
SAME HERE! HE'S HAD SOME NIGGLING BACK PROBLEMS BEFORE, BUT THIS LOOKS SERIOUS!

IT WAS! ON MONDAY MORNING, PLAYER-MANAGER ROY RACE WAS CALLED TO AN EMERGENCY MEETING OF MELCHESTER'S BOARD OF DIRECTORS!
THE DOCTOR'S FIRST REPORT SUGGESTS THAT MCKAY MIGHT HAVE TO UNDERGO SURGERY BEFORE HE'S FULLY FIT, ROY. MR SHARP HERE, IS WORRIED!
YEH, I KNOW MCKAY HAS GIVEN YEARS OF SERVICE TO THE CLUB, BUT HE IS GETTING ON A BIT! MAYBE IT'S TIME WE FOUND SOME NEW BLOOD!

WITH A STRING OF CUP MATCHES NEXT MONTH, WE CAN'T AFFORD TO HAVE A SUSPECT DEFENDER IN THE FIRST TEAM SQUAD! THE CLUB COMES FIRST, RIGHT?
PLAYERS MAKE THE CLUB, MR SHARP! PLAYERS COME FIRST!

F. C.
DIRECTOR ARTHUR SHARP WAS A PROPERTY MILLIONAIRE AT THIRTY-TWO! ROY HAD DISLIKED HIM FROM THE MOMENT THEY'D MET!
SHARP BY NAME, SHARP BY NATURE, THAT'S MY MOTTO, RACE!
SHARP BY NAME, SLY BY NATURE IS MORE LIKE IT!

ARTHUR HAS A LOT OF SOCCER CONTACTS ON THE CONTINENT, ROY! HE'S BEEN IN TOUCH WITH THE MANAGER OF MADRID ALL STARS!
THEIR TOP DEFENDER CLAUDIO LOPEZ WANTS TO PLAY IN ENGLISH FOOTBALL! HE'S A WORLD BEATER... THE 'SPANISH BULL' THEY CALL HIM OVER THERE!
YOUNG, HARD, FAST... AND EXPENSIVE! MADRID WANT A MILLION POUNDS FOR HIM! WORTH IT THOUGH, WITH DUNCAN McKAY OVER THE HILL!
WHO SAYS HE'S OVER THE HILL?
THIS IS A PRELIMINARY DOCTOR'S REPORT, THAT'S ALL! AT LEAST WE OWE IT TO BIG DUNC TO SEE HOW HE RESPONDS TO TREATMENT IN THE NEXT FEW WEEKS!
I AGREE WITH ROY, WE CAN'T BE TOO HASTY OVER A MILLION-POUND TRANSFER DEAL! WE'LL WAIT AND SEE!
DOCTOR'S REPORT
AFTERWARDS, ROY WENT STRAIGHT TO SEE THE CLUB'S PHYSIOTHERAPIST DEBBIE FOSTER!
DUNCAN'S AS HARD AS ABERDEEN GRANITE, ROY! IN MY OPINION HE SHOULD MAKE IT BACK TO FULL FITNESS WITHOUT SURGERY!
OKAY, WE'LL GO TO THE CLINIC AND TELL HIM THAT FIRST THING IN THE MORNING!
BUT WORD OF THE POSSIBLE TRANSFER HAD LEAKED OUT...
WHEN THAT SHARP CHARACTER WANTS SOMETHING, HE GETS IT, BOSS! "THE SPANISH BULL" WILL COME TO MEL PARK AND I'LL BE ON THE SCRAP-HEAP!
A DAMAGED DISC ISN'T THE END OF THE WORLD, DUNC! DEBBIE SAYS SHE CAN CURE YOU AND I BELIEVE HER!
YOU'VE ALWAYS BEEN A FIGHTER, SO FIGHT NOW! FOR ME, FOR THE CLUB, AND FOR YOURSELF!
YOU'VE ALWAYS HAD A FANCY WAY WI' WORDS, ROY RACE... AND YE'RE A HARD MAN TO SAY NO TO! SO WHEN DO WE START?

THE NEXT DAY SAW THE START OF FOUR LONG WEEKS OF INTENSIVE TREATMENT AND TRAINING!
BUT THEY WORKED! TEN DAYS BEFORE ROVERS' FIRST F.A. CUP-TIE, LEFT BACK DUNCAN McKAY WAS PRONOUNCED FULLY FIT!
I STILL SAY THE MAN IS PAST HIS BEST! WE SHOULD BUY CLAUDIO LOPEZ NOW, BEFORE SOMEBODY ELSE GRABS HIM!
PERHAPS WE STILL WILL, ARTHUR! IF McKAY DOESN'T PROVE HIMSELF IN THE CUP-TIE AGAINST WALHAM CITY, WE'LL RECONSIDER THE POSITION!
ON THE DAY OF THE MATCH...
TWO MORE MINUTES, MAC! TAKE A DEEP BREATH! TRY TO RELAX!
I-I WISH I COULD! I FEEL LIKE THIS IS THE FIRST GAME I'VE EVER PLAYED FOR MELCHESTER ROVERS! I'M A BAG OF NERVES!

SUDDENLY...
ROY... TROUBLE! ARTHUR SHARP'S JUST ARRIVED AT THE DIRECTORS' BOX WITH A MOB OF REPORTERS AND A SPECIAL GUEST! CLAUDIO LOPEZ!
WHAAAT?
HE FLEW 'THE SPANISH BULL' OVER AT HIS OWN EXPENSE TO WATCH THE GAME AND DISCUSS POSSIBLE TRANSFER TERMS!
IT'S JUST LIKE I TOLD YE, BOSS... WHAT THAT SHARP CHARACTER WANTS, HE GETS!
ARTHUR'S DONE THIS WITHOUT OFFICIAL BACKING! THERE'S BEEN NO CLUB DECISION TO SIGN CLAUDIO LOPEZ!
AND MAYBE PIGS CAN FLY! I KNOW THE WRITING ON THE WALL WHEN I SEE IT!
SHARP'S DONE THIS DELIBERATELY TO WEAR DUNCAN DOWN! I HOPE THE BIG MAN'S BIG ENOUGH TO TAKE IT!
BUT AS WALHAM CITY SWEPT DOWN THE RIGHT FLANK IN THEIR FIRST OFFENSIVE MOVE...
GNNNF!
SLOW AND HESITANT! McKAY'S LEFT THE DEFENCE WIDE OPEN!
IT'S THERRRE! A GOAL TO WALHAM IN THE FIRST FIVE MINUTES!
MELCHESTER ROVERS------0
WALHAM CITY----------1
FIFTEEN MINUTES LATER...
AAARGH!
FOUL!
OH, NO... NOW BIG MAC'S GIVEN AWAY A PENALTY!

COME ON, CITY! EAS-EEE... EAS-EEE... EAS-EEE!
'RAAAY... NUMBER TWO!

THE MELCHESTER LEFT-BACK MADE ONE BLUNDER AFTER ANOTHER!
BOOOOO! RUBBISH!
SEND HIM OFF... SUBSTITUTE HIM!

SUBSTITUTE DUNC NOW, AND HE'S FINISHED, ROY! HE'LL NEVER PLAY FIRST DIVISION FOOTBALL AGAIN!
I KNOW THAT, OLLY... WHICH MEANS THAT SOMETHING, SOMEHOW, HAS GOT TO BE DONE!

HALF-TIME CAME WITH ROVERS STILL TWO-DOWN...
DON'T TAKE IT TOO HARD, DUNC! JUST KEEP PLUGGING AWAY!
YEAH, YOUR TOUCH WILL COME BACK IN THE SECOND HALF!

LIKE HECK IT WILL! McKAY'S BEEN OUT THERE LOOKING LIKE AN OLD MAN AND PLAYING LIKE AN OLD MAN!
ARTHUR SHARP WAS RIGHT AFTER ALL... EVERY DOG HAS ITS DAY, AND YOU'VE HAD YOURS, CHUM!

YOU'RE JUST DEAD WOOD IN THIS TEAM NOW, DUNCAN... AND D'YOU KNOW WHAT YOU DO WITH DEAD WOOD...?
YOU CUT IT OUT!
HAAAAR...

RRRRG!
DON'T TAKE IT OUT ON ME, BIG MAN! TAKE IT OUT ON WALHAM CITY! PLAY FOOTBALL THE WAY YOU USUALLY DO!
OKAY, BUT NO ONE... NO ONE... EVER CALLS ME DEAD WOOD AGAIN, BOSS... AGREED?
AGREED!
PHEEEW... FOR A SECOND THERE I WAS SURE HE WAS GOING TO KNOCK YOUR BLOCK OFF, ROY!
IF HE HAD DONE, HE WOULD HAVE BEEN FINISHED! THE INSULT SEEMED TO WORK ANYWAY! BIG DUNC IS BACK IN BUSINESS, AS I THINK WE'RE ABOUT TO SEE!
AND FROM THE OPENING MOMENT OF THE SECOND HALF, LEFT BACK DUNCAN McKAY TURNED DEFENCE INTO ATTACK!
GNNNFF!
HEY, LOOK AT THAT SCOTSMAN POWER HIS WAY THROUGH! IT'S LIKE HE'S BEEN REBORN!
YOURS, ROY!
ATTABOY, DUNC... PERFECT BALL!
RAAAAY ...THE ROCKET!
KEEP'EM COMING,. MELCHESTER, THAT'S WHAT WE WANT... LOADSA-GOALS!
TWO MORE WERE ENOUGH TO SEE MELCHESTER INTO THE NEXT ROUND OF THE CUP! THE LAST ONE SCORED BY DUNCAN McKAY HIMSELF!
WAA-HAAY! BIG DUNC'S BOOMERANG SHOT ROUND THE WALL! HE FOOLED THE LOT OF 'EM!
AND AT THE FINAL WHISTLE...
NOBODY IN THE DIRECTOR'S BOX, ROY! I RECKON ARTHUR SHARP IS BOOKING CLAUDIO LOPEZ ON THE FIRST FLIGHT OUT OF THE COUNTRY!
YES, AND IF ANY TALK OF A TRANSFER COMES UP, JUST SAY THAT "THE SPANISH BULL" HAS BEEN SENT PACKING BY A GOOD OLD-FASHIONED SCOTTISH TERRIER!
The End

Bobby Robson with coach Don Howe and physio Fred Street before England's match in Yugoslavia in 1987 which they won 4–1.

THE BEST (and hardest) JOB IN THE GAME

Being the manager of England is the best – and hardest – job in the world . . . just ask Bobby Robson.

A manager of a club has only that team's supporters to satisfy. Clubs vary in size from Liverpool and Manchester United . . . to the most humble in the lower divisions.

But Bobby Robson has to satisfy the whole country. And whilst the prize for success is greater, any form of failure is greeted with far more criticism than a club manager would receive.

In October, 1988, England drew 0–0 at home to Sweden and some of the newspapers – unfairly – tore into Robson and the side.

Imagine a club manager being criticised like that after a home draw!

But the England manager is, in some ways, the luckiest man in the country because he has the pick of . . . the entire country.

The England manager doing what he enjoys most of all . . . coaching his players before an international.

England teams used to be picked by a panel of selectors . . . now it is the manager's job

He can select the best players from the best clubs without paying a penny in transfer fees.

The England manager can field a team worth millions of pounds – and it hasn't cost him anything to put the team together.

But it wasn't always the job of a manager to choose the national side.

For many years it was done by a committee and the team was picked by a number of people rather than one individual.

The selectors named 11 players plus one reserve in case of injury. There were no substitutes in those days and 20-man international squads were unheard of.

SUPREMO

Cricket still favours that type of selection, but even that sport is being urged in some quarters to move to a soccer style supremo.

The first manager of England after the War was Walter Winterbottom, but it was the appointment of Alf Ramsey – later to become Sir Alf, of course – in October, 1962, that really revolutionised England as a force in world football.

Sir Alf had transformed Ipswich from a small provincial club into League Champions and clearly had the qualities England were looking for as their manager.

Looking back on his triumphant years as England's manager, Sir Alf said: "I consider myself fortunate to have known so many great players personally.

"The qualities of the players who represented England while I was in charge were many. Their loyalty, responsibility and, above all, self-control in testing circumstances provided me with some of my most rewarding moments."

The most rewarding of all

SEE OVER

CONTINUED

came surely in July, 1966, when England beat West Germany 4–2 to win the World Cup.

English football enjoyed a boom period after that success with attendances consistently high and First Division clubs monopolising the European competitions.

Many critics believed England's team which went to the 1970 World Cup finals in Mexico was even better than the side which triumphed four years previously.

The signs were encouraging in the early games but after leading West Germany 2–0 England lost 3–2 and were out of the tournament.

While Sir Alf was a brilliant manager, he made a few enemies with his abrupt style and when England failed to qualify for the 1974 finals, the Football Association sacked the man who had given English soccer its greatest ever moment.

Joe Mercer took over as caretaker manager for a short tour of Eastern Europe before Don Revie, who had brought so much success to Leeds, was named as Sir Alf's successor.

LUCRATIVE

Few argued with the appointment of Revie. He had moulded Leeds into a formidable unit but after three years Revie defected to take over a lucrative job in the Middle East.

Ron Greenwood, whose West Ham were widely acknowledged as an exciting, attacking team, was named England's manager in 1977.

West Ham boasted Bobby Moore, Martin Peters and Geoff Hurst, three of England's 1966 World Cup heroes and while England did not qualify for the 1978 World Cup finals in Argentina, they made it to Spain four years later.

Greenwood resigned after the 1982 World Cup to hand over the reins to Bobby Robson, who, like Sir Alf, had guided Ipswich to success at home and also in Europe.

Robson has not yet been able to emulate Sir Alf and win the World Cup, but if the Tunisian referee had spotted Diego Maradona's infamous "handball" goal as Argentina beat England in Mexico, 1986 . . . who knows what might have happened?

Everyone else seemed to know that the Argentina captain had punched the ball over Peter Shilton – everyone except the match officials. It is now history

His team is worth millions – but it costs him nothing!

that Argentina went on to win the 1986 World Cup, but what a sad way for England to go out of the competition.

Although the England manager sees his team infrequently – there is usually a three-month gap between November and February for the international "close season" – it is a full-time, demanding job.

FULL-TIME JOB

The manager attends games every Saturday and usually in midweek, too. And as England players now earn their livings abroad there are trips to France, Italy and Spain, not to mention Scotland, for the manager to keep in touch with current form.

Media demands are heavy while the manager's duties extend to the grass roots of the game, not just the national team.

The England manager must be aware of the next generation of international stars and takes a big interest in the F.A.'s School of Excellence where the cream of the country's schoolkids are given a "football scholarship", combining their studies with the best coaching available.

Perhaps the biggest problem facing the manager is the overcrowded fixture list.

While many countries

SEE OVER

ABOVE
Relaxing in Copenhagen's Old Harbour before a "spying" mission on Denmark.
RIGHT
Bobby Robson checks Glenn Hoddle's pulse during altitude training in Colorado Springs before the 1986 World Cup finals in Mexico.

Bobby and Bryan Robson celebrate England's 4–1 European Championship qualifying success over Yugoslavia.

CONTINUED

postpone their League fixtures the weekend before a competitive international, it is a luxury seldom given to the England manager.

He has to keep his fingers crossed that his squad is not badly affected by injuries to key players performing for the clubs only days before a European Championship or World Cup tie.

But the chance to pick players such as Peter Shilton, Bryan Robson, Gary Lineker or Peter Beardsley makes the England manager's job so worthwhile.

Winning a major championship would make the job perfect!

England's international record up to the end of 1988

Opponents	P	W	D	L	F	A
Argentina	9	4	3	2	13	9
Australia	4	2	2	0	4	2
Austria	15	8	3	4	54	25
Belgium	17	12	4	1	66	24
Bohemia	1	1	0	0	4	0
Brazil	14	2	5	7	12	20
Bulgaria	5	3	2	0	7	1
Canada	1	1	0	0	1	0
Chile	3	2	1	0	4	1
Colombia	2	1	1	0	5	1
Cyprus	2	2	0	0	6	0
Czech'kia	10	6	2	2	19	11
Denmark	10	6	2	2	24	10
E. Germany	4	3	1	0	7	3
Ecuador	1	1	0	0	2	0
Egypt	1	1	0	0	4	0
FIFA	1	0	1	0	4	4
Finland	8	7	1	0	32	5
France	20	14	2	4	60	27
Greece	4	3	1	0	8	0
Holland	9	4	3	2	16	10
Hungary	16	10	1	5	45	17
Iceland	1	0	1	0	1	1
Israel	2	1	1	0	2	1
Kuwait	1	1	0	0	1	0
Lux'bourg	7	7	0	0	38	3
Malta	2	2	0	0	6	0
Mexico	6	3	1	2	14	3
Morocco	1	0	1	1	0	0
N. Ireland	96	74	16	6	319	80
Norway	6	5	0	1	25	4
Paraguay	1	1	0	0	3	0
Peru	2	1	0	1	5	4
Poland	5	2	2	1	6	4
Portugal	15	8	5	2	35	17
Rep. Ire.	10	5	3	2	16	9
Rest Europe	1	1	0	0	3	0
Rest World	1	1	0	0	2	11
Rumania	8	2	5	1	6	4
Saudi Arabia	1	0	1	0	1	1
Scotland	106	42	24	40	186	168
Spain	16	10	2	4	35	19
Sweden	11	6	2	3	23	14
Switz'land	15	10	2	3	37	12
Turkey	4	3	1	0	21	0
USA	5	4	0	1	29	5
USSR	7	2	2	3	7	10
Wales	97	62	21	14	239	90
W. Germany	18	9	3	6	35	24
Yugoslavia	13	4	5	4	21	19
Total	640	370	140	130	1553	705

ACTION E·X·T·R·A

GARY MEGSON (Sheff Weds)

An experienced midfield player in his second spell with Sheffield Wednesday, Gary began his career with Plymouth and has also played for Everton, Nottingham Forest (although he failed to make the first team under Brian Clough) and Newcastle.

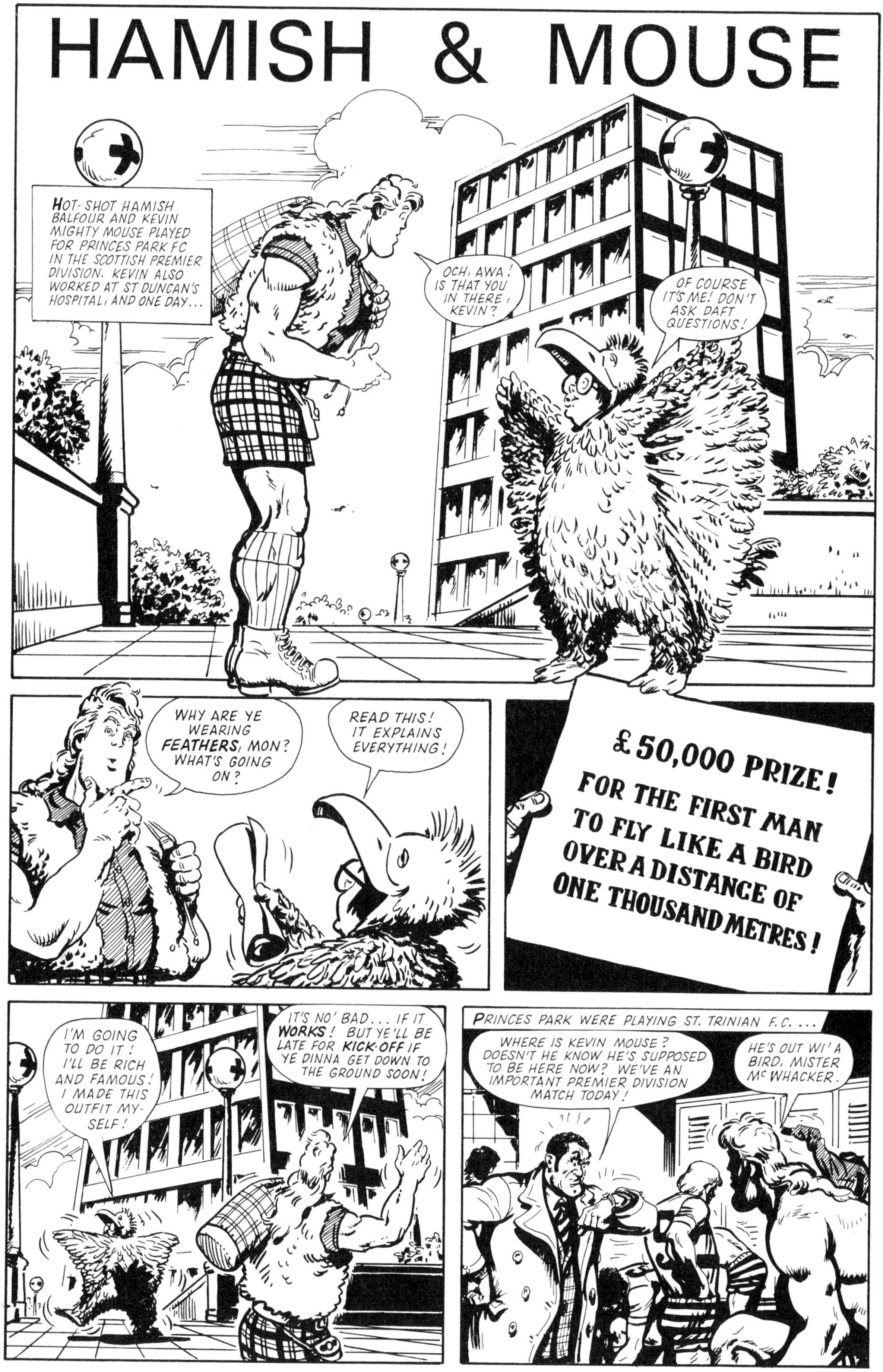

HAMISH & MOUSE

HOT-SHOT HAMISH BALFOUR AND KEVIN MIGHTY MOUSE PLAYED FOR PRINCES PARK FC IN THE SCOTTISH PREMIER DIVISION. KEVIN ALSO WORKED AT ST DUNCAN'S HOSPITAL, AND ONE DAY...

OCH, AWA! IS THAT YOU IN THERE, KEVIN?

OF COURSE IT'S ME! DON'T ASK DAFT QUESTIONS!

£50,000 PRIZE!
FOR THE FIRST MAN TO FLY LIKE A BIRD OVER A DISTANCE OF ONE THOUSAND METRES!

OUT WITH A BIRD? I WON'T HAVE MY PLAYERS GOING OUT WITH GIRLS! IT'S AGAINST THE CLUB RULES! MOUSE WILL COP IT FOR THIS!

OCH, KEVIN'S NO' OUT WI' A GIRL, BOSS! THE BIRD HE'S GOT IS A FLYING ONE... WITH WINGS!
IS THAT SO? WELL... A FOOTBALL PITCH HAS GOT WINGS! TWO OF 'EM! THAT SHOULD BE ENOUGH FOR ANYONE!
TA-RAAAA! I'M HERE! I CHANGED BEFORE I LEFT, SO I'M ALL READY TO GO, BOSS!
YE'D BETTER BE! AND THAT GOES FOR THE WHOLE TEAM! I WANT A WIN TODAY. ST TRINIAN AREN'T MUCH GOOD SO YE SHOULD DUFF 'EM UP EASILY!

STRAIGHT FROM THE KICK-OFF...
WE KNOW YOU'RE GOOD, MOUSIE! NOW GET RID OF IT!
PASS, KEVIN... BEFORE YOU LOSE THE BALL!
LOSE IT? THEY'VE GOT TO BE JOKING! NO ONE'S TAKING IT OFF ME TILL I'VE SCORED!
GOT IT!
GNUURR!

PRINCES WERE AWARDED A FREE KICK...
BOOOOOO! YE'RE A SHOW-OFF, MOUSIE!
YE'RE GETTING THE BIRD, MOUSIE!
THE BIRD? THAT'S A GOOD SIGN!

HOT-SHOT HAMISH'S GOING TO TAKE IT!
HE'LL BLAST IT STRAIGHT AT US!
OCH AWA'! THE MON'S GOT A FEARSOME SHOT!

DUCK!
A DUCK'S A BIRD! ANOTHER GOOD SIGN! EVERYONE'S THINKING ABOUT MY BIRD-MAN OUTFIT!

TAKE A SHOT, MON!
GET UP, YE COWARDS! HAVE YE ALL GONE CUCKOO!
CUCKOO! ANOTHER BIRD! IT'S AN OMEN FOR MY FLYING SUCCESS!
YEAHHHHH! MOUSE! MOUSE! MIGHTY MOUSE!
SIMPLE! NOTHING TO IT!

GIVE IT TO MOUSIE, HAMISH... GET HIM GOING DOWN THE WING! MOUSIE'S A FLYER!
HEAR THAT? ANOTHER OMEN... I'M A FLYER! I'M GOING TO WIN THAT FIFTY THOUSAND QUID FOR SURE!

IN THE PRINCES PARK DRESSING-ROOM...
FIFTY THOUSAND POUNDS FOR A BIRD-MAN WHO CAN FLY A THOUSAND METRES! SO THAT'S WHAT MOUSE IS UP TO!
£50,000 PRIZE! FOR THE FIRST MAN TO FLY 1KM.

I'LL GET MOUSE'S BIRD OUTFIT AND HAVE A GO MYSELF! I'LL COLLECT THE FIFTY THOUSAND WHILE HE'S STILL PLAYING! EASY MONEY!

I'LL WIN THE CASH AND TAKE A LONG HOLIDAY! MOUSE WILL HAVE FORGOTTEN ALL ABOUT IT BY THE TIME I GET BACK!
MEANWHILE PRINCES WERE PLAYING THE SECOND HALF... IN RAIN!
YEAAHH! THE HOT-SHOT! TWO-NIL TO PRINCES!
I DIDN'T SEE IT!
YOU'RE LUCKY! I DID! AWESOME!
AND IN MUD...
IT'S THERE! MOUSE'S SECOND! THREE-NIL!
ANOTHER GOAL? I DIDN'T SEE IT!
YE HAVNA SEEN ANYTHING YET, YE GREAT WALLIE!
IT WAS AN EASY WIN FOR PRINCES...
WHERE'S THE BOSS? I THOUGHT HE'D BE HERE TO SAY HE WAS PLEASED WI' THE WAY WE PLAYED!
HE'S HOPPED IT! HE'S GONE TO FLY IN MOUSE'S BIRD OUTFIT... AND COLLECT THE MONEY! CRAFTY DEVIL, HE IS!
IT'S NOT RIGHT! IT'S NOT FAIR! I'VE GOT TO STOP HIM! I SPENT WEEKS WORKING ON THAT BIRD OUTFIT... MAKING IT PERFECT FOR FLYING!
McWHACKER WAS ON TOP OF THE HOSPITAL TOWER-BLOCK...
ARE YOU THE OFFICIAL JUDGES READY TO WITNESS MY WORLD-SHATTERING FLIGHT?
OCH AYE!
ONE THOUSAND METRES... NO LESS, MY FEATHERED FRIEND!

READY... GO!
I'M FLYING!
DON'T GO STRAIGHT DOWNWARDS ...IT DOESNA' COUNT!

SIXTH FLOOR...
A MAN... DRESSED AS A BIRD!
FIFTH FLOOR...
HOW VERY STRANGE!

FOURTH FLOOR...
I'LL GET MY EYES TESTED WHILE I'M IN HERE!
THIRD FLOOR...
COR! WHAT A FUNNY PIGEON!

THEN KEVIN MOUSE ARRIVED...
WHO NICKED MY BIRD-OUTFIT OUT OF MY LOCKER?
MISTER McWHACKER!
HE TOLD US YOU'D GIVEN HIM PERMISSION!
HE'S FLYING IN IT, KEVIN!

HERE COMES MISTER McWHACKER NOW!

ARRRGHHHH!

WHERE IS HE? THE DIRTY CROOK!
THE EAGLE HAS LANDED!
OVER THERE!
SCHIAFFINO

DID IT WORK, BOSS? DID YOU FLY?
NO! IT WAS FLAMING USELESS! YOU'RE AN IDIOT, MOUSE!

ALL THOSE OMENS YOU WERE TALKING ABOUT ON THE PITCH CAME TO NOTHING, KEV!
YES. MAYBE A GOOD THING I DIDN'T TRY IT!

MISTER McWHACKER MUST HAVE HAD A FRIGHT!
SERVES HIM RIGHT! BIT OF A LARK, THOUGH, WASN'T IT? GET IT? BIT OF A LARK! HAW, HAW!
The End

SECOND AROU

When Ian Rush, Mark Hughes and Ray Wilkins left English football to further their careers on the Continent, it seemed as if their considerable talents would be lost to our game for a long period.

The First Division's loss was Europe's gain but, in the case of Welsh wizards Rush and Hughes, they returned after only one and two years respectively abroad while Wilkins came back after a few seasons in Italy and France to delight the followers of Glasgow Rangers.

Playing on the Continent is an ambition of many players, but the road to Europe can be tricky, as

ABOVE
Mark Hughes was a hit with Manchester United . . . a disappointment in Barcelona . . . and a hit when he returned to Old Trafford in 1988.
RIGHT
Ray Wilkins is another United old boy who came back to Britain to be a success with Rangers.

TIME
ND!

Hughes and Rush discovered.

Most fans would agree that the Liverpool ace is the best goalscorer seen in Britain during the 80's.

In his first spell with Liverpool he helped them to glory at home and in the European Cup, whilst topping the goalscoring charts regularly.

The £3 million offer Liverpool received from Juventus was too good to turn down. Italian defenders, it appeared, would be having the same sort of nightmares as their British counterparts . . . but it didn't quite work out that way.

Rush joined the worst Juventus side for years and the Turin club failed to give Rush the service he needs to bring out the best in him. If Rush didn't score as many goals as he did in England, it wasn't because he had suddenly become a bad player . . . it was because Juventus did not provide the ammunition for him to fire his bullets.

Shortly before the start of 1988/89 Liverpool brought him back to Anfield in a top secret move for a fee just under £2 million. Once Rush had recovered from a virus, he quickly showed he had lost none of his ability to make life a misery for opposing teams.

When Mark Hughes joined Barcelona for £2 million, it seemed as if he would become the spearhead of Terry Venables' team, but the Welsh striker, like Rush, found life different on the Continent.

The Spanish supporters did not appreciate Hughes' unselfish work, while the side never played to Mark's strengths. Eventually, Hughes was loaned to Bayern Munich, where he showed something like his true form.

Almost inevitably, he returned to Old Trafford in the summer of '88 and began to score goals regularly again in a United side which struggled to find consistency.

Hughes proved that he had not become a poor player in Spain. Given the right service and used in a role that suits him best, Hughes soon showed that he had lost none of the skills that had made him such a favourite with United fans before his move to Barcelona.

Ray Wilkins has not always been appreciated by everyone, but he won more than 80 caps for England and has a reputation within the game of being one of the most intelligent and influential midfield players around.

After playing for Chelsea and Manchester United, Wilkins joined AC Milan before a short, ill-fated spell with Paris Saint Germain in France.

Milan fans took Wilkins to their hearts, acknowledging him to be a midfield player of the highest class. He was in France only a few months before Graeme Souness made him the latest of the "Anglo Pack" at Glasgow Rangers.

Wilkins was soon winning rave reviews for his thoughtful style of play and there can be little doubt that he will go on to become a coach or manager.

European soccer has many advantages. It's a chance to gain more experience and prove yourself in a different type of football. The pay is also very tempting.

But many players have found it hard to transfer their skills abroad . . . yet have proved to be a huge success second time around.

Just like Ian Rush, Mark Hughes and Ray Wilkins – they have discovered that football on the Continent can be an exciting challenge, but perhaps there is no place like home!

LEFT
The return of Ian Rush to Liverpool shocked the soccer world . . . and delighted Liverpool fans.

JACK of UNITED

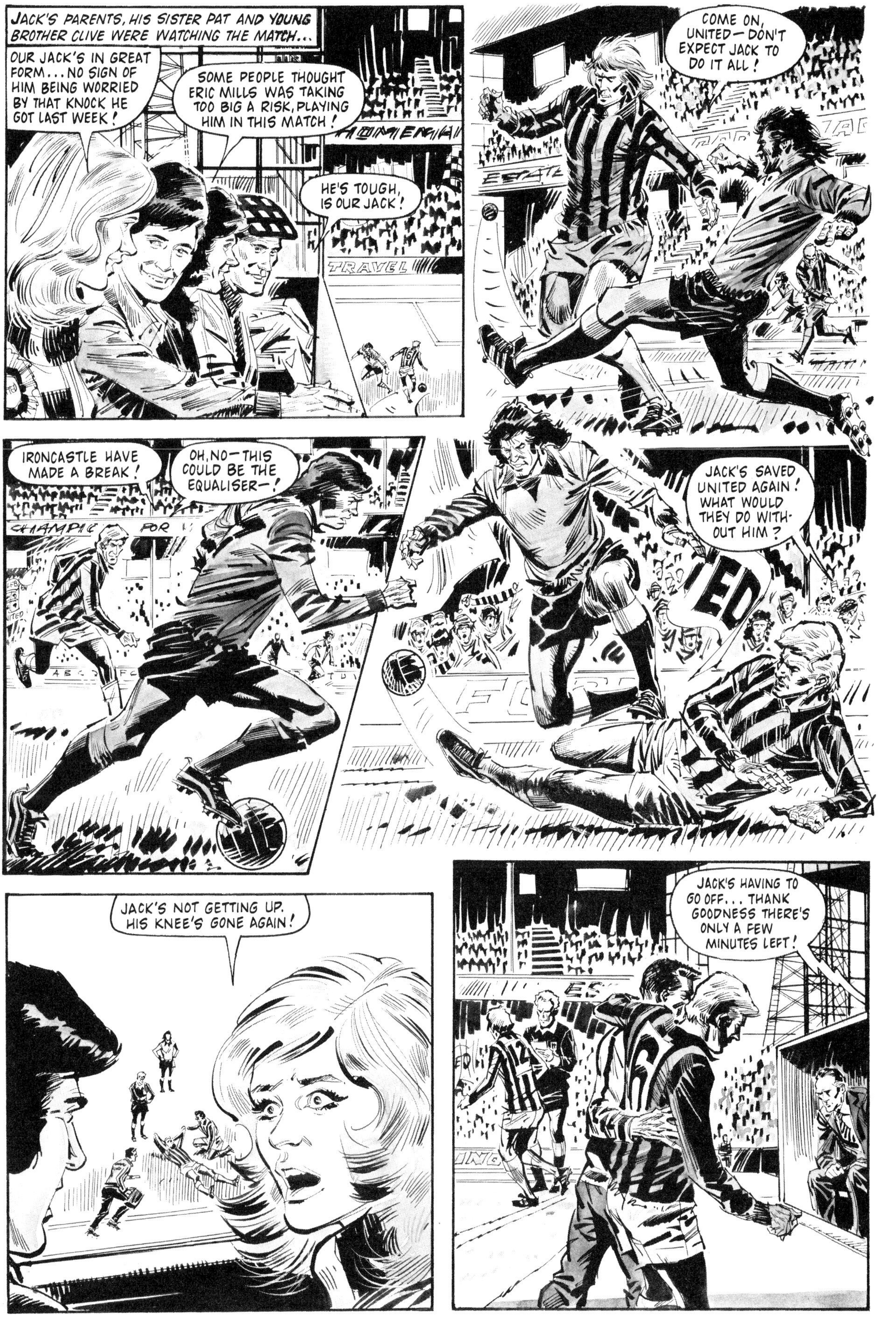

JACK'S PARENTS, HIS SISTER PAT AND YOUNG BROTHER CLIVE WERE WATCHING THE MATCH...
OUR JACK'S IN GREAT FORM... NO SIGN OF HIM BEING WORRIED BY THAT KNOCK HE GOT LAST WEEK!
SOME PEOPLE THOUGHT ERIC MILLS WAS TAKING TOO BIG A RISK, PLAYING HIM IN THIS MATCH!
HE'S TOUGH, IS OUR JACK!
TRAVEL

COME ON, UNITED—DON'T EXPECT JACK TO DO IT ALL!

IRONCASTLE HAVE MADE A BREAK!
OH, NO—THIS COULD BE THE EQUALISER—!

JACK'S SAVED UNITED AGAIN! WHAT WOULD THEY DO WITHOUT HIM?

IRONCASTLE SENSED THAT JACK'S DEPARTURE HAD SHAKEN UNITED'S CONFIDENCE, AND THEY PUT ON DESPERATE PRESSURE . . .
WHAT A TERRIBLE MISKICK!
STEADY YOURSELVES, LADS! DON'T WEAKEN NOW!
CASTLEBURN UNITED

IRONCASTLE COULD SCORE FROM THIS—UNLESS THE WHISTLE GOES!
THE REF'S LOOKING AT HIS WATCH . . .
WE MUST BE INTO INJURY TIME.

GOAAL!
OH, NO! HE'S MADE IT 2-2! HE'S PUT IRONCASTLE LEVEL!
IRONCAS
CSTLE

THERE WAS ONLY JUST TIME FOR UNITED TO KICK OFF AGAIN BEFORE THE FINAL WHISTLE . . .
UNITED WERE DEAD UNLUCKY!
IT WOULD NEVER HAVE HAPPENED IF JACK'S OLD INJURY HADN'T LET HIM DOWN!
BUT UNITED ARE BOUND TO WIN THE REPLAY AT CASTLEBURN!

BACK AT CASTLEBURN, THE UNITED TRAINER GAVE HIS VERDICT AFTER GIVING JACK A CHECK-UP . . .
NOTHING SERIOUS. BUT IF YOU WANT TO BE SURE OF HAVING HIM FIT FOR THE REPLAY, I THINK HE SHOULD STAY ON LIGHT TRAINING FOR A FEW DAYS, AND MISS THE LEAGUE MATCH AGAINST MILLGATE.

IT WAS AN UNUSUAL EXPERIENCE FOR JACK TO BE A SPECTATOR WHEN UNITED RAN OUT AGAINST MILLGATE...
DON'T LOOK SO GLUM, JACK. MILLGATE HAVE A TERRIBLE AWAY RECORD. UNITED WILL HAVE NO MORE TROUBLE — EVEN WITHOUT YOUR HELP!
BUT WITHIN FIVE MINUTES OF THE KICK-OFF...
MILLGATE ARE ONE UP! UNITED HAVE LET THEM SCORE!
WHAT ARE THEY PLAYING AT?
UNITED STRUGGLED IN VAIN TO GET A GRIP ON THE GAME, BUT AGAIN, SHORTLY BEFORE HALF-TIME...
GOAL! WE'RE TWO DOWN!
UNITED CAN'T DO A THING RIGHT!
WITHOUT JACK THEY'RE ALL TO PIECES!
BY THE END OF THE MATCH, MILLGATE HAD SCORED FOUR TIMES WITHOUT REPLY. THE CHELSEY FAMILY RETURNED HOME GLUMLY.
IF UNITED DON'T DO BETTER IN THE REPLAY, THEY'LL GET SLAUGHTERED.
IT WAS ALL TOO BAD TO BE TRUE. WITH JACK BACK EVERYTHING WILL BE DIFFERENT.
JIMMY ARRIVED HOME LATER, AFTER PLAYING AN AWAY MATCH FOR CITY.
I'VE JUST HEARD THAT AFTER TODAY'S RESULT MAX EVERETT, THE CASTLEBURN BOOKIE, IS OFFERING ODDS THAT UNITED WILL LOSE THE CUP REPLAY!
THEN HE'LL LOSE A PACKET—AND SERVE HIM RIGHT!
I'M NOT A BETTING MAN, BUT FROM WHAT I KNOW OF EVERETT HE'S NOT IN THE HABIT OF LOSING PACKETS. HE'S ONE OF THE WEALTHIEST MEN IN CASTLEBURN!

I KNOW MOST PEOPLE IN TOWN, BUT I DON'T THINK I'VE EVER MET THIS EVERETT.
YOU WOULDN'T HAVE. HE NEVER ACTUALLY **WATCHES** FOOTBALL. HE STUDIES FORM, AND BACKS HIS JUDGMENT! VERY SUCCESSFULLY!
NOT THIS TIME. HE'S RECKONED WITHOUT JACK BEING BACK IN THE TEAM.
CASTLEBURN RECORDER

BEFORE ERIC MILLS DECIDED ON UNITED'S CUP REPLAY LINE-UP, JACK WAS GIVEN A FINAL FITNESS TEST...
HE'S IN GREAT SHAPE!
THAT'S A LOAD OFF MY MIND. WE'LL BE AT FULL STRENGTH THEN!

THEN PHIL HUGHES, UNITED'S SKIPPER, CAME IN...
I HEAR YOU'RE ON YOUR OWN TONIGHT, JACK. HOW ABOUT COMING TO A MOVIE AND THEN BACK HOME WITH ME FOR A MEAL?
SOUNDS GREAT.

MY MOTHER'S VISITING AN AUNT, WITH PAT AND CLIVE. DAD'S AWAY ON A BUSINESS TRIP, JIMMY'S MAKING AN OVERNIGHT TRIP WITH CITY, AND I WAS EXPECTING TO HAVE TO SPEND AN EVENING WATCHING TELLY ALL ON MY OWN!

IT WAS LATE WHEN JACK RETURNED TO AN EMPTY HOUSE. HE HAD JUST PUT THE CAR AWAY, WHEN...
AAAARGH!
A HIT AND RUN DRIVER!

HE'S BEEN KNOCKED OUT, BUT OTHERWISE HE DOESN'T SEEM TOO BADLY HURT. I'D BETTER GET HIM INTO THE HOUSE!

JACK SEARCHED THE POCKETS OF THE UNKNOWN VICTIM TO TRY TO IDENTIFY HIM...
THERE'S NOTHING ON HIM TO SHOW WHO HE IS OR WHERE HE COMES FROM, BUT— PHEW—THIS WALLET IS ABSOLUTELY **STUFFED** WITH CASH!

THEN...
OOOH... MY HEAD!
YOU'D BETTER TAKE IT EASY FOR A BIT. I'M JUST MAKING SOME COFFEE—OH, BY THE WAY, THERE'S YOUR WALLET!

A COUPLE OF SMASHING LOOKING GIRLS. YOUR SISTERS?
ONE OF THEM'S MY MOTHER. SHE'D BE FLATTERED.

YOU'VE BEEN VERY KIND. I'M MOST GRATEFUL. I'M FEELING FINE NOW. I'LL BE ON MY WAY.
HOLD ON. I'LL GET THE CAR OUT AND DRIVE YOU HOME.

I WOULDN'T DREAM OF PUTTING YOU TO THAT TROUBLE AT THIS TIME OF NIGHT. IT ISN'T FAR AND I WAS JUST OUT FOR A BREATH OF AIR BEFORE TURNING IN WHEN THAT IDIOT DRIVER KNOCKED ME DOWN!
AT LEAST LET ME PHONE FOR A TAXI!

WHEN THE TAXI ARRIVED...
THANKS FOR EVERYTHING— YOU'VE DONE ME A REAL GOOD TURN.
IT WAS NOTHING. GLAD TO BE OF HELP.
STREWTH! IF I HADN'T HEARD THAT WITH MY OWN EARS, I'D NEVER HAVE BELIEVED IT!

LATER THAT NIGHT, THE CAB DRIVER TOLD A STRANGE STORY TO SOME OF HIS PALS . . .
I GET THIS CALL TO JACK CHELSEY'S HOUSE, AND WHO SHOULD COME OUT BUT **MAX EVERETT, THE BOOKIE!** IT WAS OBVIOUS JACK HAD BEEN DOING HIM FAVOURS. AND THAT'S NOT ALL. WHEN I GOT EVERETT HOME HE GAVE ME SOME VERY STRANGE INSTRUCTIONS . . .

JACK DISMISSED THE INCIDENT FROM HIS MIND, SO THAT WHEN THE FAMILY RETURNED HE DIDN'T EVEN MENTION IT. BUT AFTER HE HAD LEFT HOME FOR THE REPLAY AT UNITED'S STADIUM, HIS MOTHER AND SISTER GOT A SURPRISE.
I'VE BEEN ASKED TO DELIVER THESE TO THE TWO LADIES OF THE HOUSE.
WHAT A LOVELY SURPRISE!

THIS BRACELET MUST HAVE COST A BOMB!
I'VE NEVER OWNED SUCH A NECKLACE. I WONDER WHICH OF OUR MENFOLK HAS BEEN BUYING US PRESENTS? IT MUST BE TO CELEBRATE SOMETHING. BUT WHAT?
THE STORY TOLD BY THE CAB DRIVER, AND EXAGGERATED BY HIS MATES, SPREAD LIKE WILDFIRE THROUGH CASTLEBURN. AT KICK-OFF TIME JACK WAS ONE OF THE FEW WHO HADN'T HEARD IT, BUT MANAGER ERIC MILLS SOON SPOKE UP . . .
IT'S BEING SAID THAT YOU'RE ACCEPTING EXPENSIVE PRESENTS FROM MAX EVERETT, JACK!
THAT'S DAFT. I'VE NEVER MET THE MAN.
OF COURSE WE TAKE YOUR WORD, JACK. BUT, WITH EVERETT STANDING TO LOSE A PACKET IF WE WIN THE REPLAY, IT SOUNDS NASTY!

THE RUMOUR REACHED THE CITY GROUND, WHERE JIMMY WAS THE LAST TO HEAR IT . . .
WELL, I FIRST HEARD IT FROM OUR MILKMAN.
I CAN'T BELIEVE IT OF JACK CHELSEY!
SSH. HERE COMES JIMMY. DON'T MENTION IT IN FRONT OF HIM!

DON'T MENTION **WHAT** IN FRONT OF ME? WHAT'S THIS ABOUT JACK?
YOU WERE BOUND TO HEAR SOONER OR LATER. THERE'S A RUMOUR GOING ROUND THAT MAX EVERETT HAS BEEN GIVING HIM EXPENSIVE PRESENTS TO MAKE SURE UNITED LOSE THE REPLAY!

YOU DARE TO SAY THAT MY BROTHER TAKES BRIBES FROM A BOOKIE? I'M GOING STRAIGHT HOME TO SORT THIS OUT. I'LL CLOBBER ANYONE WHO DARES SAY A WORD AGAINST JACK.
STEADY ON, JIMMY. NO-ONE SAID WE BELIEVED IT!
THE REST OF THE FAMILY WERE WAITING FOR JIMMY TO JOIN THEM FOR THE MATCH. PAT AND HER MOTHER WERE PROUDLY WEARING THEIR EXCITING GIFTS.
ISN'T IT SMASHING?
WHICH OF YOU GAVE US THESE EXPENSIVE PRESENTS?
NOT ME.
NOR ME. IT'D TAKE A YEAR'S POCKET-MONEY!
OH HECK! THEN THERE'S SOMETHING IN THE RUMOUR. WHAT'S JACK BEEN UP TO?
YOU'LL HAVE TO GO ON WITHOUT ME. SOMETHING IMPORTANT HAS COME UP THAT I'VE GOT TO SEE TO RIGHT AWAY.
GRANGE
HERE THEY COME.
JIMMY'S GOING TO MISS A MARVELLOUS GAME.
I WONDER WHERE HE WENT DASHING OFF TO? HE'S SO IMPULSIVE.
IRONCASTLE OPENED BY PUTTING UNITED UNDER TERRIFIC PRESSURE.
JACK... CLEAR IT!

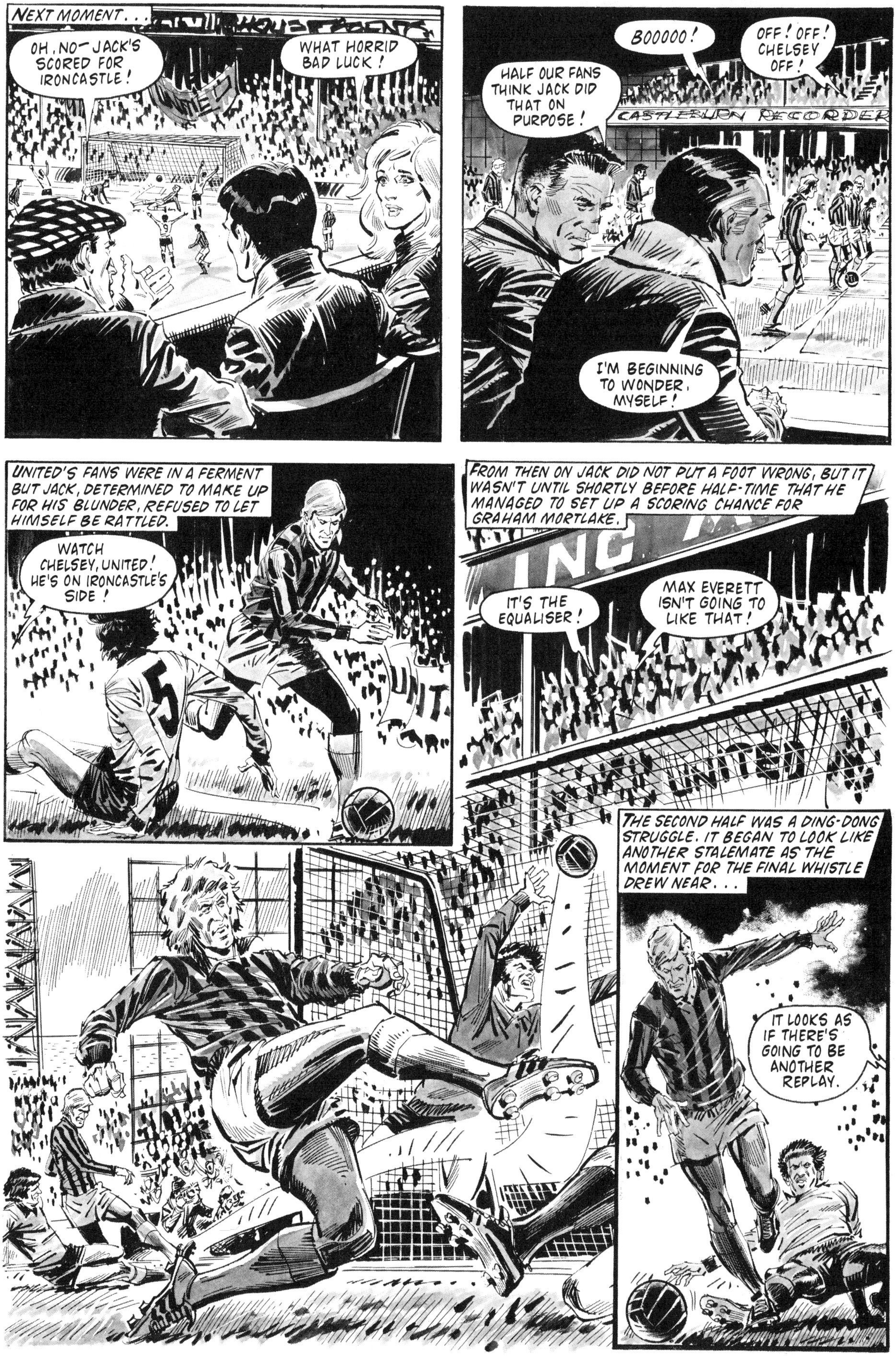

UNITED'S FANS WERE IN A FERMENT BUT JACK, DETERMINED TO MAKE UP FOR HIS BLUNDER, REFUSED TO LET HIMSELF BE RATTLED.

WATCH CHELSEY, UNITED! HE'S ON IRONCASTLE'S SIDE!

FROM THEN ON JACK DID NOT PUT A FOOT WRONG, BUT IT WASN'T UNTIL SHORTLY BEFORE HALF-TIME THAT HE MANAGED TO SET UP A SCORING CHANCE FOR GRAHAM MORTLAKE.

IT'S THE EQUALISER!

MAX EVERETT ISN'T GOING TO LIKE THAT!

THE SECOND HALF WAS A DING-DONG STRUGGLE. IT BEGAN TO LOOK LIKE ANOTHER STALEMATE AS THE MOMENT FOR THE FINAL WHISTLE DREW NEAR . . .

IT LOOKS AS IF THERE'S GOING TO BE ANOTHER REPLAY.

AND THEN...
IT'S THERE!
THE WINNER!
GOOD OLD JACK!

THANKS TO JACK, UNITED HAD WON 2-1!
A GREAT PERFORMANCE, JACK. YOU CERTAINLY SCOTCHED THOSE RUMOURS. I MUST CONFESS THAT AT ONE TIME EVEN I WAS A BIT UNEASY.
IT'S A COMPLETE MYSTERY TO ME HOW SUCH A STORY EVER GOT STARTED.

JIMMY!
I'VE BROUGHT SOMEONE TO SEE YOU. HE'S BEEN OUT OF TOWN AND ONLY JUST GOT BACK, SO HE DIDN'T HEAR THE RUMOURS.
HOME TEAM

HELLO. WHAT A PLEASANT SURPRISE. NICE TO SEE YOU AGAIN.
SO YOU DO KNOW MAX EVERETT, AFTER ALL!

WE ONLY MET ONCE. I DIDN'T THINK TO ASK HIS NAME.
I DIDN'T WANT TO EMBARRASS JACK BY TELLING HIM. BUT I WANTED TO SHOW MY APPRECIATION AND I KNEW IT WAS NO USE OFFERING JACK SOMETHING FOR HIMSELF. IT NEVER OCCURRED TO ME THAT LOUD-MOUTHED CAB DRIVER WOULD GOSSIP!

THAT GOAL OF HIS HAS COST ME A SMALL FORTUNE. BUT I WOULDN'T HAVE IT ANY OTHER WAY. I'D GLADLY LOSE MORE THAN THAT TO PROVE TO THIS TOWN THAT JACK CHELSEY IS A REAL SPORTSMAN.
READ THE STORY ABOUT JACK'S BROTHER JIMMY ON PAGE 66—IT'S FULL OF ACTION!

PUSH NUM

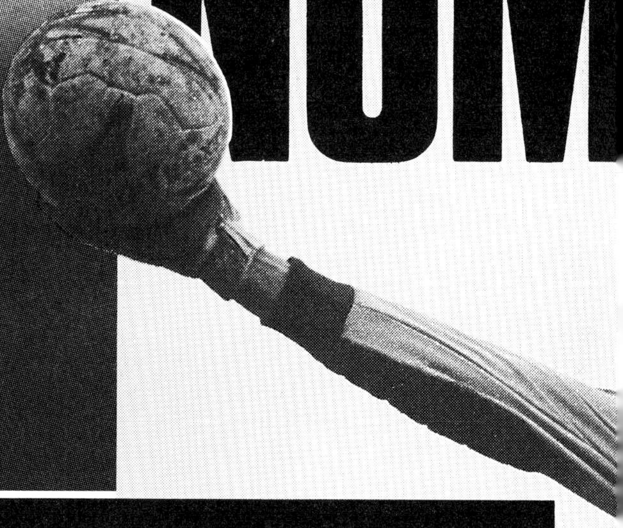

Peter Shilton has been the undisputed number one England goalkeeper for many years. Critics have written him off . . . but he's made them eat their words by playing as well as ever – which is very good! Here we pay tribute to this great goalkeeper and take a look at some of the players who hope to be his successor.

LEFT
Shilton is a model professional and still stays behind for extra training.

ING FOR BER 1

Peter Shilton is the King of England's goalkeepers.

He has won more than 100 caps for his country and the total would be considerably more had England manager Ron Greenwood not decided to alternate Shilts and his rival Ray Clemence for a while before the 1982 World Cup finals.

Shilton won his first full international cap against East Germany back in 1971. England won 3–1 and in the side that day was another young hopeful called Emlyn Hughes, who went on to win so much success with Liverpool before turning to a career in television.

The reason behind Shilton's ability to play at the highest level for almost 20 years is his dedication to training. Many players are blessed with outstanding skills but fail to make the most of them because they do not work hard enough at their game.

No player puts more into the daily routine of training than Peter the Great. Even now, he will often ask a teammate to stay behind to give him extra shooting practice.

This single-minded attitude has enabled Shilton to maintain a level of consistency which has made him such a respected goalkeeper.

To Shilts, there is no such thing as an unstoppable goal. Every time he is beaten, he goes over the move and asks himself if he could have done more to stop the goal . . . he is always striving for perfection.

In recent seasons critics have said that Shilton is nearing the end of his career . . . but he starts a new season and plays better than ever.

If England have had some disappointing results in the past

ABOVE
David Seaman made his England debut against Saudi Arabia in 1988

PUSHING FOR NUMBER 1

LEFT
Another huge clearance from Dave Beasant, now with Chelsea.

year, no-one can point the finger at Shilton.

After the failure in the 1988 European Championship there were calls for new players, but how could Bobby Robson drop Shilton, who was playing to the same high standards he has set himself over the years?

Chris Woods is a fine goalkeeper. He has benefited by his move to Glasgow Rangers, where he has had valuable experience of playing in Europe . . . something denied to those in the English Football League.

Woods has also been helped by working closely with Shilton over the years. Whilst Woods must be frustrated that he hasn't had more chances, he would be the first to acknowledge that Shilton has maintained his position as top of the stops.

It is likely that one day Woods will become England's regular first choice goalkeeper, but as Shilton has said that he wants to play in the 1990 World Cup finals, Woods may have to wait a while longer.

There are other outstanding goalkeepers in England who would probably have had more

ROY RACE VIEW:

"Shilts is still the master!"

international recognition had they been born elsewhere.

There's QPR's highly-rated David Seaman, who won his first cap in Saudi Arabia in 1988.

Dave Beasant led Wimbledon to the FA Cup Final, where they beat Liverpool, before joining Newcastle for £850,000, and then moving on to Chelsea less than one season later. Steve Ogrizovic has been an unsung hero for Coventry while Nigel Martyn has shown with the Under-21's that he is one for the future.

But until Shilton quits, the younger pretenders may have to bide their time before they can replace the master goalkeeper.

LEFT
Chris Woods has benefited from training with Shilton.

RIGHT
Steve Ogrizovic has been Coventry's Mr Consistency.

FAR RIGHT
Nigel Martyn is one of the most promising young goalkeepers in England.

THE MOON-ROCK KID
CHUMPTOWN UNITED WERE BOTTOM OF THE FOURTH DIVISION AND HADN'T WON A GAME FOR TWO MONTHS. CHARLIE FLASHMAN, THEIR MANAGER, HOPED FOR A GOOD RUN IN THE CUP TO RESTORE THEIR FORTUNES... BUT LUCK WAS AGAINST THEM!
LOOK AT 'EM... FIRST TEAM GOALIE ...BUSTED LEG! SECOND TEAM... BUSTED ARM. JUNIOR TEAM... DROPPED HIS WEIGHT-LIFTING GEAR ON HIS TOES!
WE'VE HAD IT, BOSS... EVEN IF WE COULD FIND ANOTHER GOALIE, WE GOT NO MONEY TO BUY HIM!
FAT MAN
IF YOU'RE AFTER A GOALKEEPER, MATE, YOU SHOULD HAVE A LOOK AT OUR FRED FLOGGIT! PLAYS IN THE HOSPITAL TEAM... FANTASTIC!
RUBBISH, MORE LIKE IT!
WON'T DO NO HARM LOOKING AT HIM, BOSS!
MAGAZINES · BOOKS
CHOCS
THE HOSPITAL TEAM WERE PLAYING THAT AFTERNOON...
WHICH ONE'S THE GOALIE? CAN'T SEE HIM ANYWHERE.
BIG BLOKES, AIN'T THEY, BOSS?
AND THEN...
HE'S THE GOALIE? HE'S TOO SHORT! IF THE GRASS WAS MUCH LONGER, HE'D GET LOST!
HE'S ONLY A SCHOOL KID!
THE GAME BEGAN...
YOU WATCH THIS, MATE... FRED'S MARVELLOUS AT CORNERS!
I'M WATCHING!

WHAT A JUMP!
HE-HE JUMPED HIGHER THAN THEIR HEADS!
FAT MAN
2
9
A FEW MOMENTS LATER...
THAT'S BEATEN HIM.. HE'S GOING THE WRONG WAY!
4
8
BUT...
BRRRRRMMMMMMMMMM!
STONE THE CROWS! HOW DID HE DO THAT?
IT-IT'S LIKE HE WAS FLYING, BOSS!
THIS BOY IS FANTASTIC! I'VE NEVER SEEN ANY-THING LIKE IT!
WE'VE GOTTA SIGN HIM, BOSS! HE COULD WIN THE CUP FOR US!
AT THE END OF THE GAME...
HOW WOULD YOU LIKE TO PLAY FOR CHUMPTOWN, SON? WE COULD SIGN YOU ON AS AN AMATEUR!
WE WANT YOU FOR OUR CUP SIDE, LAD! WHADDYA SAY?
FAT MAN
WELL, I WOULDN'T MIND...IF I CAN GET THE TIME OFF FROM SCHOOL!

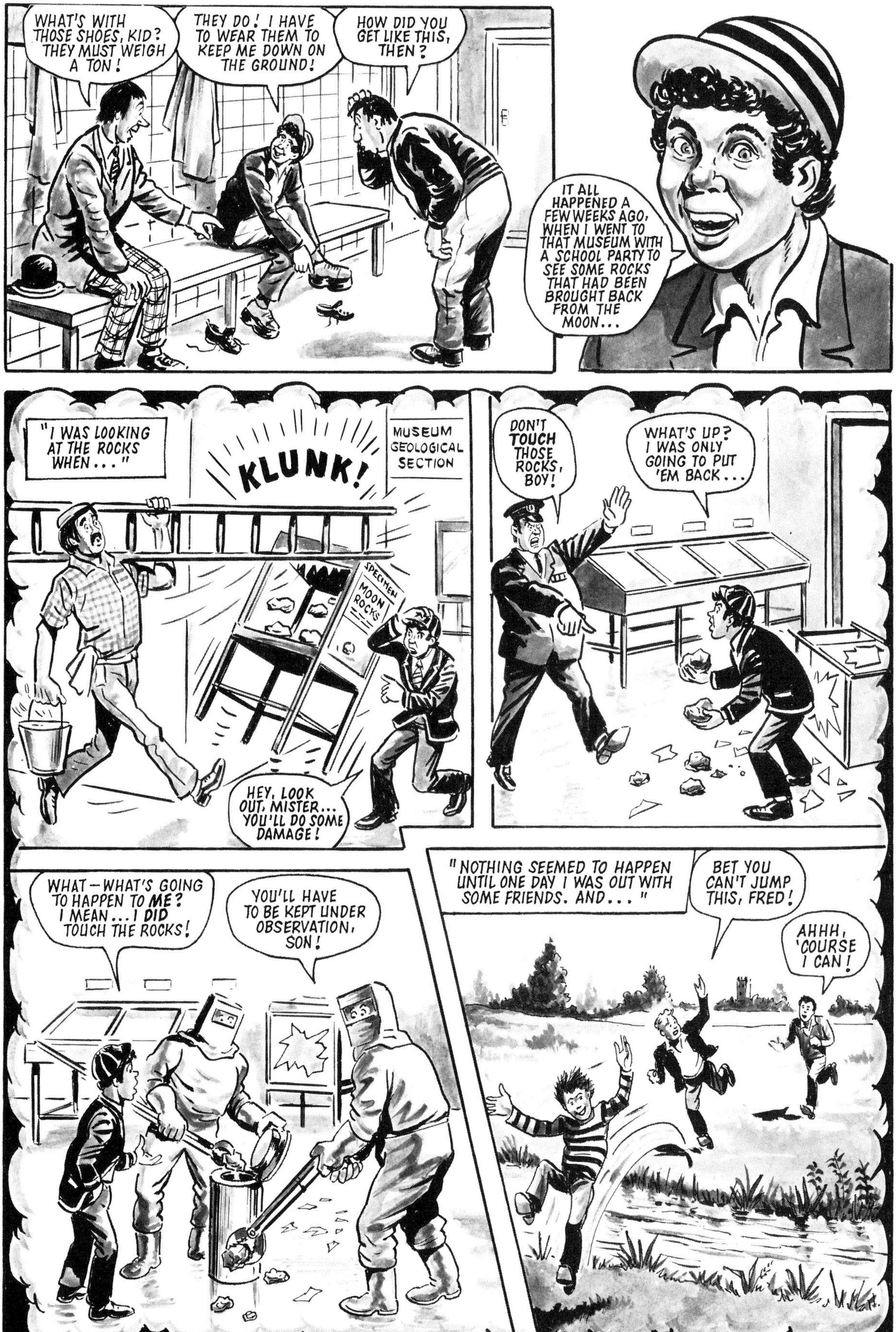

"I WAS LOOKING AT THE ROCKS WHEN..."
KLUNK!
MUSEUM GEOLOGICAL SECTION
SPECIMEN
MOON ROCKS
HEY, LOOK OUT, MISTER... YOU'LL DO SOME DAMAGE!

DON'T **TOUCH** THOSE ROCKS, BOY!
WHAT'S UP? I WAS ONLY GOING TO PUT 'EM BACK...

WHAT—WHAT'S GOING TO HAPPEN TO **ME**? I MEAN... I **DID** TOUCH THE ROCKS!
YOU'LL HAVE TO BE KEPT UNDER OBSERVATION, SON!

"NOTHING SEEMED TO HAPPEN UNTIL ONE DAY I WAS OUT WITH SOME FRIENDS. AND..."
BET YOU CAN'T JUMP THIS, FRED!
AHHH, 'COURSE I CAN!

COR, LOOK AT FRED!
WHAT A JUMP!

I FOUND I COULD JUMP FOR MILES... AND SORT OF TURN ROUND IN MID-AIR AND GO IN A DIFFERENT DIRECTION! I SEEMED TO BE AS LIGHT AS A FEATHER!

IT'S THE MOON-ROCK! HE'S LOST A LOT OF HIS GRAVITY!
SEMI-WEIGHTLESS!
JUST AS THOUGH HE WERE IN OUTER SPACE!
HAVE TO WAIT UNTIL IT WEARS OFF!

THAT'S WHY I HAVE TO WEAR THESE SHOES... TO KEEP ME DOWN!
A WEIGHTLESS GOALKEEPER! MARVELLOUS! HE CAN OUT-JUMP ANY STRIKER IN THE GAME!
FAT MAN
FLY ACROSS THE GOAL TO GET TO ANY SHOT!

AND...
SPORTS NEWS
NEW GOALKEEPER
CHUMPTOWN SIGN MOON-ROCK BOY IN GOAL AS AMATEUR!
Wonder goalkeeper, aged twelve, to play in Chumptown's First round Cup-tie at Greystone Park.
It was reported today that this young lad has a

CHUMPTOWN UNITED WON THEIR FIRST ROUND TIE...
HURRAHHHH!
GOOD OLD FRED!
WATCH THAT BOY JUMP!
8
3

SECOND ROUND... THIRD... FOURTH... INTO THE SEMI-FINALS...
WHAT A SAVE!
THE MOON-BOY'S GOT IT! TERRIFIC!

UNTIL...
SPORTING WORLD
CHUMPTOWN UNITED IN FINAL
Fourth Division Chumptown have reached Wembley with an amazing record of eight goals For.....and none Against! No one has been able to beat twelve-year-old wonder boy Fred Floggit, the Moon-Rock Boy!

THE NIGHT BEFORE THE FINAL...
GET A GOOD NIGHT'S SLEEP IN, SON. WE WANT YOU AS FRESH AS A DAISY TO KEEP 'EM OUT IN THE FINAL!
OKAY, MISTER FLASHMAN - GOODNIGHT!
IN THE MIDDLE OF THE NIGHT...
OOOO-ERR! I FEEL ALL FUNNY!

AND...
THE-THE WEIGHT'S COME BACK! I'M NOT WEIGHTLESS ANY MORE ... MY FEET FEEL AS HEAVY AS LEAD!
CRA-A-SHH!

I-I CAN'T JUMP! I-I'M BACK TO NORMAL. IT'S LIKE THE DOCTOR SAID... IT'S WORN OFF!

AND... I'VE GOT TO PLAY IN GOAL... AT WEMBLEY... IN THE CUP FINAL! TOMORROW!

FRED WAS TOO FRIGHTENED TO TELL CHARLIE FLASHMAN...
HERE THEY COME! HURRRAAHHH!
CAN'T JUMP AN INCH!

SOON AFTER THE GAME STARTED...
GOOOAALLLL! ONE UP TO RANGERS!
I CAN'T GET NEAR IT...
3

WHAT'S WRONG WITH HIM? HE DIDN'T JUMP! HE SHOULD HAVE GOT THAT EASILY!
HE HARDLY GOT OFF THE GROUND, BOSS!

WHEN A PLAYER WAS INJURED, FAT MAN RUSHED OUT TO FRED...
FAT MAN
IT'S NO GOOD, MISTER... I'VE LOST MY LEAP! I'M LIKE ANY-ONE ELSE. THE MOON-ROCK EFFECT HAS WORN OFF!
WORN OFF? IN THE MIDDLE OF THE CUP FINAL? YOU CAN'T DO THIS TO US, KID!

BUT CHARLIE HAD AN IDEA...
CHANGE HIM OVER WITH SIDNEY AT CENTRE-FORWARD. SID'S A GOOD GOALIE... HE'LL DO BETTER THAN THAT STUPID KID!
YEAH! GOOD THINKING, BOSS!
FAT MAN
WHAT DO I HAVE TO DO? I'VE NEVER PLAYED AS A STRIKER BEFORE!
JUST CHASE THE BALL, SON. AND WHEN YOU GET IT... BOOT IT AS HARD AS YOU CAN AT THEIR GOAL. NOTHING TO IT!
9
FRED DID AS HE WAS TOLD...
ROT MY FOOTBALL SOCKS, FATMAN! LOOK AT THAT KID RUN... HE'S FASTER THAN A GREYHOUND!
HE'S A LOT BLOOMING FASTER THAN THEIR DEFENDERS, BOSS!
I-I'VE NEVER MOVED SO QUICKLY IN ALL MY LIFE! IT'S THOSE HEAVY BOOTS I'VE BEEN WEARING! NOW I'VE GOT RID OF 'EM... I CAN REALLY MOVE!
GOOOOOALLLLLLL!
THE MOON-ROCK KID'S SCORED!
THAT WAS A RIGHT MOON ROCKET SHOT!

SIDNEY IN GOAL DIDN'T HAVE AS MUCH LUCK, THOUGH...
GOOOALLLLL! TWO-ONE TO RANGERS!
NOW THAT FRED HAD FOUND OUT HE COULD RUN, HOWEVER, HE KEPT DOING IT!
GOOOALLLLL! TWO-ALL!
THEY CAN'T CATCH THAT KID!
EVERY TIME HE GETS IT, IT'S A GOAL!

AS OFTEN AS SID LET IN A GOAL, FRED SCORED ANOTHER!
GOOOOOALLLL!

WHEN IT WAS ALL OVER!
SPORTS SE
CHUMPTOWN WIN 14 - 13! CUP FINAL SENSATION
Fred Floggit the wonder Moon-Rock boy scored fourteen goals at Wembley today after coming out of goal to play in the attack. Twelve-year-old Fred says he doesn't want to turn professional and is retiring from football at the end of the season.

IF YOU'D TAKEN UP HIGH-JUMPING, YOU'D HAVE WON THE WORLD RECORD EASILY, FRED!
YEAH, I SUPPOSE I COULD, I NEVER THOUGHT OF THAT...

STILL, I'D RATHER HAVE MY CUP WINNER'S MEDAL. I MEAN, I'LL NEVER GET ANOTHER CHANCE TO WIN ONE, WILL I?
IT'S GOLD!
SMASHING!
IT ALL SEEMS LIKE A DREAM, REALLY. BUT IT CAN'T BE... CAN IT?
The End

ACTION E·X·T·R·A

IAN CROOK (Norwich)

A promising youngster with Spurs, Ian could not command a regular place at White Hart Lane and joined Norwich for £80,000 in 1987. He has enjoyed the responsibility of being the Canaries' playmaker and has become one of the most influential midfielders in the First Division

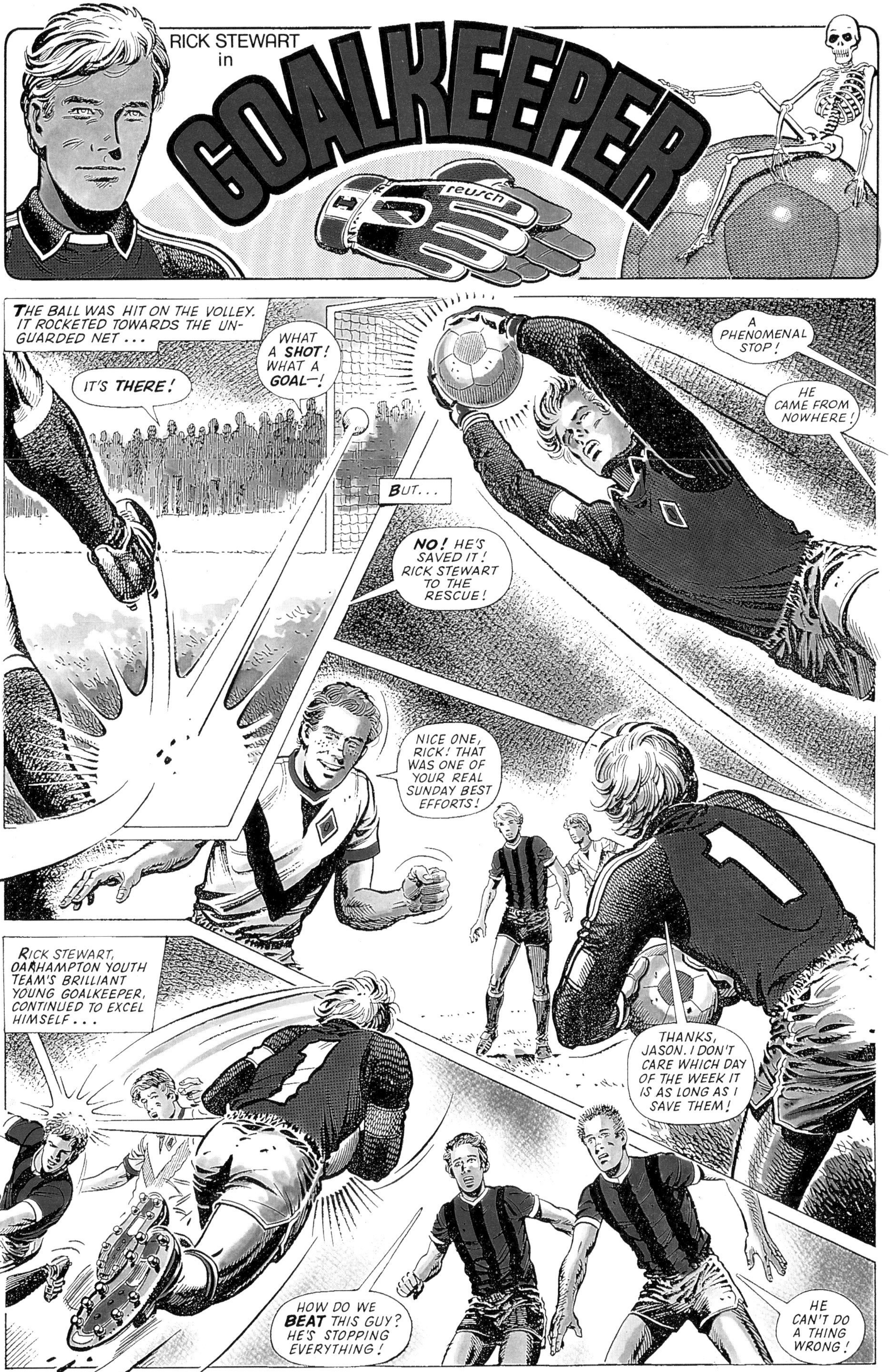

THE BALL WAS HIT ON THE VOLLEY. IT ROCKETED TOWARDS THE UNGUARDED NET . . .

IT'S **THERE**!

WHAT A **SHOT**! WHAT A **GOAL**—!

BUT . . .

A PHENOMENAL STOP!

HE CAME FROM NOWHERE!

NO! HE'S SAVED IT! RICK STEWART TO THE RESCUE!

NICE ONE, RICK! THAT WAS ONE OF YOUR REAL SUNDAY BEST EFFORTS!

THANKS, JASON. I DON'T CARE WHICH DAY OF THE WEEK IT IS AS LONG AS I SAVE THEM!

RICK STEWART, OAKHAMPTON YOUTH TEAM'S BRILLIANT YOUNG GOALKEEPER, CONTINUED TO EXCEL HIMSELF . . .

HOW DO WE **BEAT** THIS GUY? HE'S STOPPING EVERYTHING!

HE CAN'T DO A THING WRONG!

UNTIL, TEN MINUTES AFTER THE INTERVAL...
ATHLETIC HAVE HIT THE POST!
IT'S REBOUNDING!
IT'S GONE IN! WE'VE SCORED!
IN OFF RICK STEWART!

FROM THAT MOMENT ON, THE FLOODGATES SEEMED TO OPEN...
ATHLETIC SCORE AGAIN! 2-0!
AN OWN GOAL! STEWART COULD DO NOTHING ABOUT THAT!

AND AGAIN! 3-0!
A WICKED BOUNCE!
IT WAS SPINNING... GOING AWAY FROM HIM ALL THE TIME!

THE FINAL RESULT... A 0-4 DRUBBING FOR OAKHAMPTON!
BAD LUCK, GOALIE. YOU DIDN'T DESERVE TO LOSE BY THAT MARGIN!
NOT TO WORRY. EVERY 'KEEPER HAS DAYS WHEN THINGS DON'T GO RIGHT.

YOU'RE SUPPOSED TO BE MY LUCKY MASCOT, FRED. CAN YOU DO A BIT BETTER FOR ME NEXT WEEK, PLEASE?

BUT IT WAS NOT TO BE...
GOOOAAAL!
THE BALL HIT A RUT AND BOUNCED BADLY!
POOR OLD RICK— NOTHING'S GOING RIGHT FOR HIM!

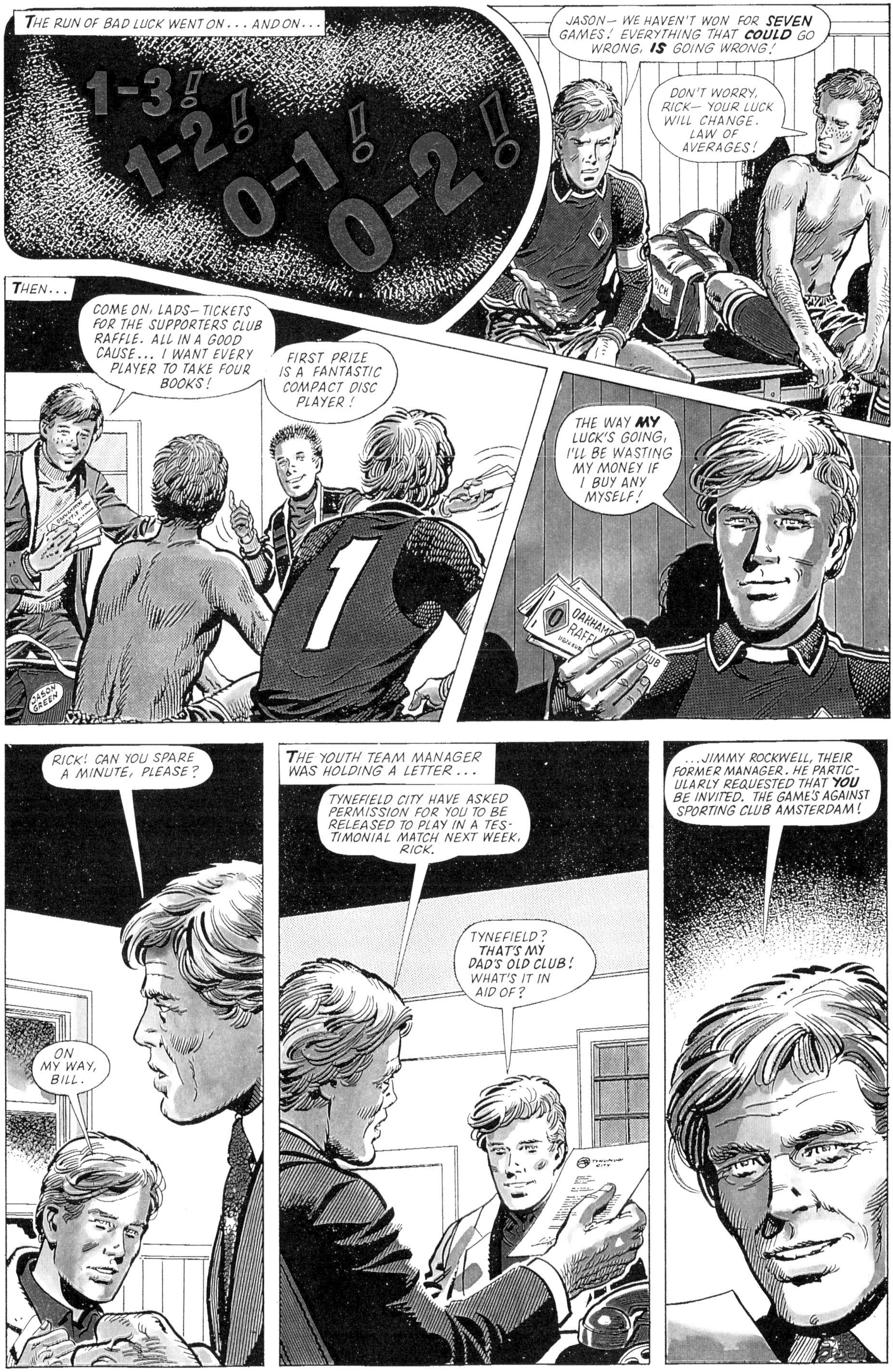

THE RUN OF BAD LUCK WENT ON . . . AND ON . . .

1-3! 1-2! 0-1! 0-2!

JASON— WE HAVEN'T WON FOR **SEVEN** GAMES! EVERYTHING THAT **COULD** GO WRONG, **IS** GOING WRONG!

DON'T WORRY, RICK— YOUR LUCK WILL CHANGE. LAW OF AVERAGES!

THEN . . .

COME ON, LADS— TICKETS FOR THE SUPPORTERS CLUB RAFFLE. ALL IN A GOOD CAUSE . . . I WANT EVERY PLAYER TO TAKE FOUR BOOKS!

FIRST PRIZE IS A FANTASTIC COMPACT DISC PLAYER!

JASON GREEN

THE WAY **MY** LUCK'S GOING, I'LL BE WASTING MY MONEY IF I BUY ANY MYSELF!

THE EUROPEAN CUP HOLDERS? OH, NO! THAT MEANS THERE'LL BE A FULL HOUSE AT TYNEFIELD. I CAN'T POSSIBLY PLAY!
WHY? YOU'RE NO STRANGER TO SENIOR FOOTBALL...

I'M HAVING A TERRIBLE RUN OF LUCK, BILL... YOU KNOW THAT. I'LL LOOK A REAL LEMON IF I LET A STACK OF GOALS IN!

BILLY BAXTER KNEW HOW SUPERSTITIOUS RICK WAS...
COME ON, RICK. NOT SCARED, ARE YOU? A BIG BOY LIKE YOU...
OF COURSE NOT...

EVERY PLAYER NEEDS LUCK... BUT SOMETIMES YOU HAVE TO MAKE YOUR OWN LUCK, ESPECIALLY IN GOAL! YOU CAN'T BE CHICKEN IN SOCCER...

RICK ROSE TO THE BAIT...
I'M NOT CHICKEN! BAD LUCK OR NOT, I'LL PLAY IN JIMMY ROCKWELL'S TESTIMONIAL GAME!
GOOD.

RICK WAS GREETED BY JIMMY ROCKWELL HIMSELF...
NICE OF YOU TO COME, RICK. YOU'RE LOOKING MORE LIKE YOUR FATHER EVERY DAY!
I JUST WANT TO PLAY LIKE HE DID, MISTER ROCKWELL.
...ESPECIALLY TONIGHT!

THE TYNEFIELD TEAM WAS LITTERED WITH STAR NAMES...
THERE'S DAVE BRYANT OF EXTON CITY AND ENGLAND. COLIN McPHEE OF SCOTLAND. I'M IN HIGH CLASS COMPANY TONIGHT!

IF THERE WAS ONE TIME I NEEDED HELP FROM YOU, FRED, IT'S...
RICK STARED DOWN— AND FELT HIS STOMACH LURCH!
HE-HE'S NOT IN MY BAG! I MUST HAVE LEFT HIM BEHIND IN THE RUSH TO GET HERE!
reusch

HE GOT READY IN A DAZE...
WITHOUT LUCKY FRED, I HAVEN'T A **CHANCE!** THIS MATCH WILL BE A **DISASTER**... MY WORST EVER! I KNOW IT!

LOOK— THERE'S RICK STEWART!
FANCY A YOUTH TEAM PLAYER APPEARING WITH ALL THESE STARS!
THE DUTCH SIDE PLAYED FLUID, ATTACKING FOOTBALL...
WHAT A TEAM!
LOVELY TO WATCH! THEY'LL CHALK UP A **CRICKET SCORE** TONIGHT!
I FEEL SORRY FOR YOUNG STEWART!

BUT...
OH, A **FANTASTIC** SAVE!
HE MUST HAVE **SPRINGS** IN HIS BOOTS!
GREAT STOP! WELL PLAYED, LAD!

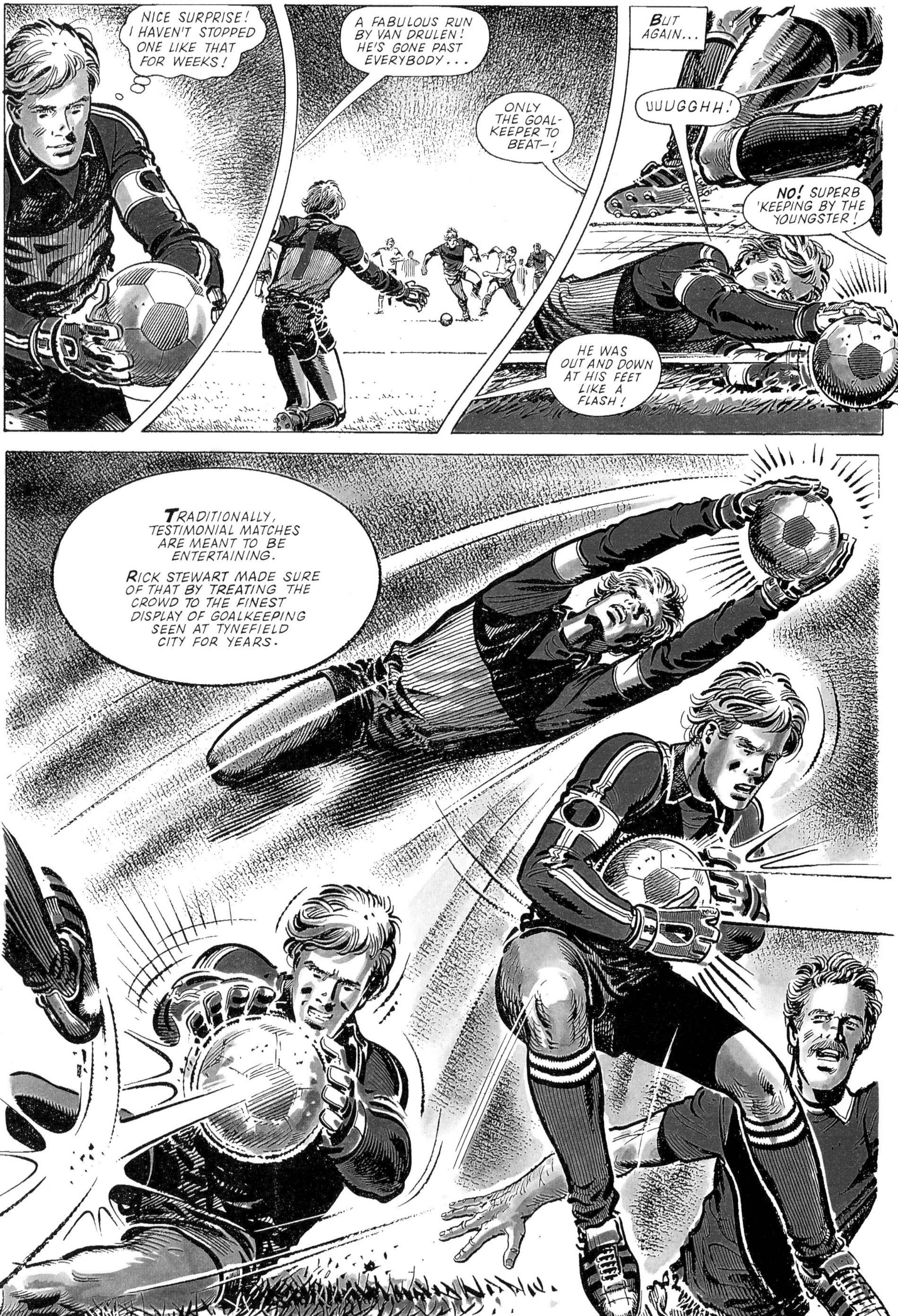

TRADITIONALLY, TESTIMONIAL MATCHES ARE MEANT TO BE ENTERTAINING.

RICK STEWART MADE SURE OF THAT BY TREATING THE CROWD TO THE FINEST DISPLAY OF GOALKEEPING SEEN AT TYNEFIELD CITY FOR YEARS.

VALT

TYNEFIELD
BACK AT OAKHAMPTON . . .
YOU WERE DEAD RIGHT, BILL. GOALKEEPERS CAN MAKE THEIR OWN LUCK. I KEPT A BLANK SHEET LAST NIGHT– WITHOUT MY LUCKY MASCOT!
GREAT, RICK. WHAT DID I TELL YOU?
BUT HOW DO YOU EXPLAIN THIS? I FORGOT TO SELL ANY OF MY BOOKS IN THE SUPPORTERS CLUB RAFFLE. I HAD TO BUY THEM ALL MYSELF.
SO–?
I WON FIRST PRIZE!
RAFFLE
FOOTBALL CLUB
THE END

A-Z of FOOTBALL

"I'VE GOT A FEELING THE REF. WILL ABANDON IT BECAUSE OF THE MUD."

RANGERS 2, UNITED 1, HOOLIGANS ARRESTED 22....

"CAN I HAVE MY FIFTY PENCE PIECE BACK, PLEASE ?"

"THE MANAGERS COMPLIMENTS, SIR, HE SAYS LAY OFF THE CIGARS 'COS IF WE HAVE ANY MORE INJURIES YOU'LL BE PLAYING NEXT WEEK !"

"THEY'RE REFUSING TO PLAY EXTRA TIME UNLESS THEY GET PAID OVERTIME !"

F FOR FREE-KICK

"THAT WILL TEACH HIM TO GIVE AWAY FREE-KICKS FOR SHOUTING !"

G FOR GOALIE
" IT'S NOTHING PERSONAL, SID, WE NEVER KISS GOALKEEPERS!"

H FOR HALF-TIME
TEA
" I THOUGHT I'D HAVE MY HALF-TIME DRINK OUT HERE, THE MANAGER ALWAYS SHOUTS AT ME IN THE DRESSING ROOM!"

I FOR INJURY

J FOR JINX TEAM

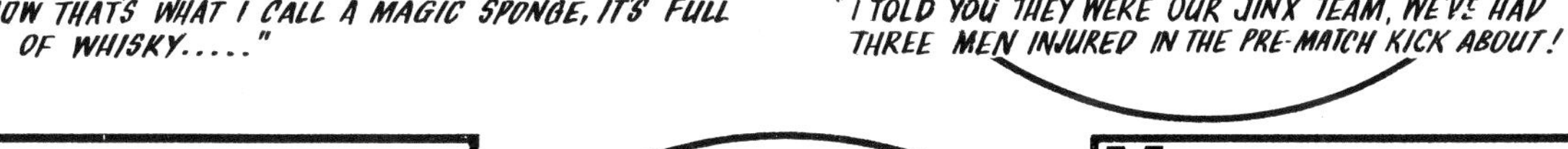
" NOW THAT'S WHAT I CALL A MAGIC SPONGE, IT'S FULL OF WHISKY....."
" I TOLD YOU THEY WERE OUR JINX TEAM, WE'VE HAD THREE MEN INJURED IN THE PRE-MATCH KICK ABOUT!"

K FOR KIT
" SORRY, FRED, IT'S A MIX-UP AT THE LAUNDRY AND WE HAVEN'T ANY SPARE KIT..."

L FOR LINESMAN
Colin Whitlock
" I DON'T KNOW, I WASN'T WATCHING!"

M FOR MANAGER
"AS A MANAGER IT'S MY JOB TO PASS ON THE BENEFITS OF MY GREAT EXPERIENCE AND SUBTLE SKILLS – SO I WANT YOU TO BELT THE BALL DOWN THE MIDDLE AND RUN LIKE CRAZY!"

N FOR NAMETAKING

"I'M SORRY, MUMMY SAID I MUSTN'T GIVE MY NAME TO STRANGE MEN!"

O FOR OWN GOAL

"YOU CAN TELL WHAT A ROTTEN SEASON THEY'VE HAD, THEIR FULL-BACK IS THEIR LEADING SCORER WITH FIVE OWN-GOALS"

P FOR PENALTY

"WE'VE HAD A LOT MORE PENALTIES SINCE WE SIGNED ARTHUR, HE WENT TO DRAMA SCHOOL!"

Q FOR QUESTION

"..... AND NOW THE PLAYERS ARE ASKING THE REF. TO CONSULT THE LINESMAN....."

R FOR REFEREE

" I TOLD YOU THAT REF. WAS BIASED...... "

S FOR STRIKER

"I KNOW WE BOUGHT HIM AS A STRIKER, BUT THIS IS RIDICULOUS!"

"OOOH GOODY! YOU'VE WON! DO
I POST THE COUPON, NOW....?

ROY RACE'S

Q.23

How well do you know soccer? As usual, Roy poses plenty of questions to make you scratch your heads!

Q.8

Q.18

SOCCER QUIZ

1 Who captained England to their 1966 World Cup success – Bobby Charlton or Bobby Moore?

2 Where do Burnley play their home games?

3 Who are Keith Hackett and John Martin?

4 Who are the Football League's sponsors?

5 From which club did Russell Osman join Southampton in 1988?

6 What does a captain wear to signify he is the team's skipper?

7 Which club plays at Boundary Park?

8 Before playing for Liverpool, John Aldridge was at which club?

9 In which city do Hearts and Hibernian play?

10 Where will the 1994 World Cup finals be played?

11 If David Speedie was tackled by Tony Adams, which clubs would be playing?

12 Which club in the north east does athlete Steve Cram support?

13 What are the names of the two Milan clubs?

14 True or False: Bobby Robson once played for Fulham?

15 Who were the winners of the last European Championship . . . and who did they beat in the final?

16 What is wrong with this statement: White Heart Lane is the home of Tottenham Hotspur?

17 Which club plays at Griffin Park – Bradford, Brighton or Brentford?

18 What position does Middlesbrough's Gary Pallister play?

19 Which London club ended a 103-year wait by finally winning promotion to the First Division in 1988?

20 Name the two clubs who play their home matches at Selhurst Park.

21 Which French club did Mark Hateley and Glenn Hoddle join?

22 Manchester City play in . . . which colour shirts?

23 Who headed Wimbledon's winner against Liverpool in the 1988 FA Cup final?

24 What is the nickname of Luton Town?

25 Craven Cottage is the home of . . . which club?

26 Who won the 1982 World Cup – was it Italy or West Germany?

27 Which trophy is Celtic's Roy Aitkin holding aloft?

28 A young Arsenal midfield player made his full England debut by coming on as a substitute against Denmark in September, 1988. Was it Michael Thomas, Paul Davis or David Rocastle?

Q.27

CONTINUED OVER LEAF

29 They play in green and white hooped jerseys . . . in 1967 they became the first British club to win the European Cup . . . who are they?

30 Which club is nicknamed the Hammers?

31 Who succeeded Graham Taylor as manager of Watford?

32 If you were at Portman Road, which club would you be watching?

33 Name the two Harfords at Luton.

34 Who did Gordon Strachan play for before Manchester United?

35 Which Scottish club plays at Tannadice Park?

36 How many goals did Charlie Nicholas score for Arsenal in the 1987 Littlewoods Cup final?

37 In which country do Bayern Munich play?

38 Welsh strikers Mark Hughes and Ian Rush had disappointing spells with foreign clubs – can you name them?

39 What is the name of the Everton defender with the Belgian surname?

40 Who play at the Dell?

41 In which stadium do Scotland play their home matches?

42 And where do Northern Ireland play their home games?

43 True or false: West Ham United play at Ufton Park?

44 Who is the manager of the Republic of Ireland?

45 With which Midlands club did Gary Lineker begin his career?

46 Howard Kendall quit Everton to take over at which Spanish club?

47 Who manages England's Under-21 team?

48 Name the player Nottingham Forest manager Brian Clough refers to as "the number nine."

49 Who won the Mercantile Credit Centenary Trophy final played at Villa Park in October, 1988?

50 Which club plays at Ayresome Park?

51 True or false: PSV Eindhoven play in the Dutch League?

52 When Ossie Ardiles was released by Spurs, which other London club did he join?

53 What is the name of Brighton's stadium?

54 Who plays at Ninian Park?

Q.45

55 Steve Williams left Arsenal for which club in the summer of 1988?

56 What Spanish club did Terry Venables manage before Tottenham?

57 Which club plays at Plough Lane?

58 Which country does Marco van Basten play for?

59 Which other London club did Arsenal's George Graham manage?

60 Who was the manager of Liverpool before Kenny Dalglish – Bob Paisley or Joe Fagan?

Q.56

ANSWERS

1. Bobby Moore. 2. Turf Moor. 3. They are both Football League referees. 4. Barclays. 5. Leicester. 6. An armband. 7. Oldham. 8. Oxford United. 9. Edinburgh. 10. USA. 11. Coventry v Arsenal. 12. Sunderland. 13. AC and Inter. 14. True. 15. Holland beat the USSR. 16. It's White HART Lane. 17. Brentford. 18. Centre half. 19. Millwall. 20. Crystal Palace and Charlton. 21. Monaco. 22. Light blue. 23. Lawrie Sanchez. 24. The Hatters. 25. Fulham. 26. Italy defeated West Germany. 27. Scottish Premier. 28. David Rocastle. 29. Celtic. 30. West Ham. 31. Dave Bassett. 32. Ipswich. 33. Ray Harford (manager) and Mick Harford (striker). 34. Aberdeen. 35. Dundee Utd. 36. Two. 37. West Germany. 38. Rush joined Juventus from Liverpool and Hughes joined Barcelona from Manchester United. 39. Pat van den Hauwe. 40. Southampton. 41. Hampden Park. 42. Windsor Park. 43. It's UPTON Park. 44. Jack Charlton. 45. Leicester. 46. Athletic Bilbao. 47. Dave Sexton. 48. It's Nigel Clough, his son. 49. Arsenal 2, Manchester United 1. 50. Middlesbrough. 51. True. 52. QPR. 53. Goldstone Ground. 54. Cardiff. 55. Luton. 56. Barcelona. 57. Wimbledon. 58. Holland. 59. Millwall. 60. Joe Fagan.

ACTION E·X·T·R·A

DAVID SPEEDIE
(Coventry)

After spells with Barnsley and Darlington, the Scot joined Chelsea where he gained a reputation as a skilful and fiery forward. He signed for Coventry for £750,000 in 1987 and developed into an outstanding midfield player.

SPOT THE STARS

Big match action between Manchester United and Everton. Everton's Pat Nevin is tackled by United and England star Bryan Robson. Would you have recognised them both without reading their names first?

JIMMY OF CITY
JIMMY CHELSEY PLAYED FOR FAMOUS CASTLEBURN CITY, AND HIS BROTHER JACK FOR THEIR GREAT LOCAL RIVALS, CASTLEBURN UNITED. CITY WERE PLAYING AT HOME TO STOCKBURN IN THE THIRD ROUND OF THE CUP, AND WERE ALREADY LEADING 2-1 WHEN JIMMY CROSSED A HIGH BALL INTO THE GOALMOUTH, AND PADDY MURPHY LEAPT TO HEAD IT HOME.
THAT MAKES IT 3-1 TO CITY!
WHAT A GREAT HEADER FROM PADDY!
JIMMY'S CROSS MADE IT EASY FOR HIM!

JIMMY'S PARENTS WERE WATCHING THE GAME, ALONG WITH HIS SISTER PAT AND YOUNGER BROTHER CLIVE...
IT'S TOO LATE FOR STOCKBURN TO COME BACK FROM BEHIND NOW. THE GAME'S ALMOST OVER. CITY ARE INTO THE FOURTH ROUND!
I'VE LOST COUNT OF THE NUMBER OF TIMES PADDY HAS SCORED WITH HEADERS FROM JIMMY'S CROSSES. THEY'VE GOT SOMETHING GOING FOR THEM THAT WILL TAKE THEM TO WEMBLEY!
THE ONLY DANGER IS THAT CITY RELY TOO MUCH ON THOSE TWO. AT UNITED IT'S DIFFERENT. THEY DON'T ONLY HAVE TO DEPEND ON JACK AND SOME OTHER PLAYER TO GET RESULTS.

ALMOST AS THE FINAL WHISTLE WAS ABOUT TO BLOW, PADDY MURPHY WAS CAUGHT IN A CRUNCHING TACKLE.
ARRRGH!
GOSH! THAT MUST HAVE HURT!

PADDY WAS HELPED OFF. MOMENTS LATER, WHEN THE GAME ENDED, JIMMY SPOKE ANXIOUSLY TO MANAGER IAN CLARK.
WHERE'S PADDY?
WE PACKED HIM OFF FOR AN X-RAY—JUST AS A PRECAUTION.

LATER THAT EVENING...
SUPER MEAL, MUM!
EVERYONE FINISHED? BRING A TRAY, PAT, AND YOU CAN ALL HELP CLEAR AWAY.
SOMEONE AT THE FRONT DOOR. I'LL GO.

IS JIMMY IN?
HE'S EXPECTING US!
GOSH. HE DID MENTION IT. BUT HE DIDN'T SAY ANYTHING ABOUT EXPECTING GIANTS.

WE'RE GOING DOWN TO THE COMMUNITY CENTRE. WE'RE THINKING OF STARTING A CASTLEBURN BASKETBALL CLUB. I'M HOPING TO INTEREST IAN CLARK IN IT AS A TRAINING AID FOR CITY.

BASKETBALL? YOU? I WAS JUST WONDERING WHETHER THERE WAS ANYTHING GOOD ON THE TELLY. BUT THIS I MUST SEE. IT'LL BE MORE FUN THAN ANYTHING ON THE BOX!
I'M COMING, TOO!
LET'S ALL GO!

DO YOU KNOW ANYTHING ABOUT THIS GAME?
NOT MUCH. BUT I RECKON THAT IF YOU'RE GOOD AT ONE BALL GAME YOU CAN SOON PICK UP ENOUGH ABOUT OTHERS TO GET SOME FUN OUT OF THEM.
INSTRUCTOR

CUT THAT OUT, JIMMY CHELSEY. YOU'RE NOT PLAYING IN A CUP-TIE NOW. THERE'S NO BODY CONTACT ALLOWED IN THIS GAME.

HARD LUCK, JIMMY... YOU NEED LONGER LEGS!
OR A PAIR OF STILTS!

WHAT WAS THAT YOU WERE SAYING, JIMMY, ABOUT BEING ABLE TO PLAY ANY BALL GAME?
PHEW! THIS ISN'T SO EASY AS IT LOOKS.

I THINK I'M BEGINNING TO GET THE HANG OF IT NOW!

WE SHOULD GET DANGER MONEY!

I DON'T THINK IAN CLARK WOULD APPROVE OF THIS. YOU'D BETTER PACK UP BEFORE YOU BREAK SOMETHING!
I'M NOT GIVING UP THAT EASILY. THIS COULD BE A GREAT GAME ONCE YOU MASTER IT!

WHEN JIMMY REPORTED FOR TRAINING ON MONDAY, THERE WAS BAD NEWS FROM IAN CLARK...
PADDY HAS A BADLY PULLED MUSCLE. HE'LL BE OUT OF THE TEAM FOR OUR NEXT GAME AGAINST WESTHILL — MAYBE LONGER. TOM FIELD HERE WILL TAKE HIS PLACE.

WE'VE BEEN RELYING HEAVILY ON PADDY GETTING HIS HEAD TO JIMMY'S CROSSES INTO THE BOX. MAYBE WE'LL HAVE TO RETHINK OUR TACTICS...
LET'S SEE IF TOM AND I CAN GET SOMETHING GOING FOR EACH OTHER, FIRST.
JIMMY BEGAN TO GIVE THE RESERVE PLAYER THE CHANCE TO SHOW WHAT HE COULD DO.
CASTLEBURY AUTOS
HE'S GOT A LOT TO LEARN!
WE'LL HAVE TO WORK HARD ON HIM THEN, BETWEEN NOW AND SATURDAY, WON'T WE?
Cleaners
EAST
THAT'S BETTER.
BUT NOT GOOD ENOUGH! PADDY WOULD HAVE STEERED IT WIDE OF THE 'KEEPER—BUT THIS LAD IS NO PADDY MURPHY.
NOPQR
NOW HE SEEMS TO BE IMPROVING.
I HOPE SO. BUT HE WAS ALLOWED PLENTY OF TIME, AND PLENTY OF ROOM. A TRAINING EXERCISE IS ONE THING... PUTTING IT INTO PRACTICE UNDER MATCH PRESSURE IS ANOTHER!
LATER...
WE'VE JUST HEARD THE DRAW FOR THE FOURTH ROUND. WE'RE AWAY TO LANCHESTER.
LANCHESTER, AWAY? PHEW, THAT'LL BE A TOUGH ONE!

HEY, I'VE JUST REMEMBERED. WE'RE AT HOME TO LANCHESTER IN THE LEAGUE THE WEEK BEFORE THE FOURTH ROUND. IT'LL MAKE A USEFUL REHEARSAL.
I JUST HOPE WE HAVE PADDY BACK BY THEN.
THE WESTHILL MATCH WAS A DISAPPOINTMENT TO THE CITY FANS.
FIELD LEFT IT TOO LATE BEFORE HE JUMPED.
PADDY WOULD HAVE HAD THAT IN THE BACK OF THE NET— NO BOTHER.
MINUTES LATER SKIPPER TREVOR SCOTT WAS YELLING AT TOM FIELD.
TOM— FIND SPACE.
CITY
JIMMY HELD THE BALL TOO LONG.
IT WASN'T HIS FAULT. HE WAS TRYING TO GAIN TIME FOR FIELD TO GET INTO POSITION.
FIELD IS TAKING TOO LONG TO READ THE GAME. HE JUST ISN'T USED TO FIRST DIVISION PACE.
IT WAS BEGINNING TO LOOK AS IF THE GAME WOULD END IN A GOAL-LESS DRAW WHEN, LATE IN THE MATCH, JIMMY WENT WEAVING THROUGH ON HIS OWN...
IT'S A GOAL!
JIMMY'S GOT ONE AT LAST!
HE SHOULD HAVE DONE THAT LONG AGO INSTEAD OF WASTING TIME TRYING TO BRING FIELD INTO THE GAME!

WHEN THE GAME ENDED, TOM FIELD WAS DEJECTED...
YOU MUST BE FED UP WITH ME, JIMMY. YOU CARVED OUT SOME TERRIFIC CHANCES, AND I WASTED THEM!
DON'T WORRY ABOUT IT — YOU JUST NEED MORE EXPERIENCE.
DURING THE FOLLOWING WEEK JIMMY PESTERED THE CITY'S TRAINER FOR NEWS OF PADDY MURPHY'S RECOVERY.
HOW'S PADDY COMING ON?
HE'LL BE BACK ON LIGHT TRAINING IN A DAY OR TWO BUT IT WOULD BE TOO MUCH OF A GAMBLE TO RISK PLAYING HIM IN THE LEAGUE MATCH AGAINST LANCHESTER.
YOU'LL HAVE TO MANAGE AGAIN WITH TOM FIELD — AS LONG AS I'M FIT FOR THE CUP-TIE.
AS JIMMY WAS LEAVING THE GROUND...
JIMMY — COULD I ASK YOU TO DO ME A FAVOUR?
THAT DEPENDS ON WHAT IT IS.
IT WAS "STRINGY" BEAN, ONE OF THE CITY APPRENTICES...
IT'S THIS BASKETBALL CLUB. I'VE NEVER PLAYED, BUT I'M DEAD KEEN TO HAVE A GO. HOW DO I JOIN?
YOU'VE CERTAINLY GOT THE BUILD FOR IT. COME ROUND TO MY HOUSE THIS EVENING AND I'LL TAKE YOU DOWN THERE AND INTRODUCE YOU TO THE LADS.
THAT EVENING, BEFORE LEAVING HOME, JIMMY TELEPHONED THE CITY MANAGER.
IAN, CAN YOU SPARE TIME TO POP ROUND TO THE CENTRE THIS EVENING? I THINK I CAN SHOW YOU SOMETHING INTERESTING.
STRINGY BEAN WAS GIVEN A FRIENDLY RECEPTION.
YOU CERTAINLY LOOK AS IF YOU OUGHT TO MAKE A GOOD BASKETBALL PLAYER. LET'S SEE HOW YOU GET ON.
COUGAR

NO, NO. YOU'RE NOT SUPPOSED TO USE YOUR **FEET**!

THAT'S NOT RIGHT EITHER!
BUT HE MADE A GREAT JOB OF GETTING UP TO THE BALL.

STRINGY WAS TAKING A LONG TIME TO GET USED TO THE RULES.
STOP FOOLING ABOUT!
WE'RE NOT PLAYING RUGGER!
GRAB THE IDIOT!

JIMMY, WHAT'S GOING ON?
HELLO, IAN. I THOUGHT I MIGHT INTEREST YOU IN MAKING BASKETBALL A PART OF OUR TRAINING PROGRAMME!

ARE YOU OUT OF YOUR MIND? I'VE GOT ENOUGH TROUBLES. YOU COULD BREAK A LIMB. I DON'T WANT TO SEE ANY OF MY PLAYERS WITHIN A MILE OF THIS PLACE.

SATURDAY ARRIVED, GIVING CITY THE CHANCE TO TAKE THE MEASURE OF THEIR CUP-TIE OPPONENTS OF THE FOLLOWING WEEK.
LOOK AT THOSE TWO DEFENDERS. THEY'RE GIANTS. I BET WE'RE IN FOR SOME TROUBLE FROM THEM.
CITY

JIMMY WAS SOON PROVED RIGHT.
IT'S HOPELESS. TOM WOULD NEED STILTS TO GET ABOVE THOSE TWO. EVEN JIMMY CAN'T FIND THE ANSWER.
CHAMP
LANCHESTER
CITY

WHAT A DISASTER. WE'LL JUST HAVE TO HOPE THAT IT WILL ALL BE DIFFERENT NEXT WEEK WHEN WE GET PADDY BACK.

ON MONDAY THE CITY TRAINER DECIDED THAT PADDY WAS FIT TO RESUME TRAINING.
IPC MAGA
TAKE IT EASY TO BEGIN WITH, PADDY.

THEN...
WHAT'S HE DONE TO HIMSELF?

THE MUSCLE HAS BROKEN DOWN AGAIN. HE'S OUT OF THE GAME.
THIS IS A CALAMITY. I WAS RELYING ON HIM TO OUTSMART THE LANCHESTER DEFENCE. TOM FIELD COULDN'T COPE — AND THERE'S NO-ONE ELSE.
OH YES, THERE IS!

THERE'S STRINGY BEAN. HE AND I WOULD HAVE TO WORK HARD ALL THE WEEK AT WAYS TO GET ROUND LANCHESTER'S TWO FULL BACKS, BUT HE COULD DO IT. HE'S TALLER THAN EITHER OF THEM.
IT'S A GAMBLE, AND A TERRIBLE ORDEAL FOR THE LAD, BUT I GUESS WE'VE NO CHOICE.
WHEN SATURDAY CAME, AND CITY RAN OUT ON TO THE LANCHESTER PARK, STRINGY BEAN WAS ON THE VERGE OF PANIC.
JIMMY, I'M PETRIFIED.
THERE'S NO NEED TO BE. JUST KEEP YOUR EYE ON ME AND CONCENTRATE ON THE THINGS WE'VE BEEN PRACTISING ALL THE WEEK.
THE TESTING MOMENT FOR STRINGY CAME SOON AFTER KICK-OFF...
I CAN HARDLY BEAR TO LOOK. YOUNG STRINGY HAS BEEN DREADING THIS, ALL THE WEEK. IF HE MESSES IT UP HE'LL GO TO PIECES.
BUT STRINGY DIDN'T MESS IT UP!
IT'S A GOAL!
CITY ARE IN FRONT.
THAT'S JUST THE TONIC STRINGY NEEDED. NOW WE CAN START TO TAKE LANCHESTER APART.
AT THE END OF THE GAME THE CHELSEY FAMILY DROVE HOME IN HIGH SPIRITS.
CITY ARE THROUGH TO THE FIFTH ROUND. LANCHESTER HAVEN'T TAKEN SUCH A HAMMERING AT HOME FOR AGES!
3-0, AND THAT LAST GOAL OF JIMMY'S WAS A DREAM.
I BET IAN CLARK HAS CHANGED HIS MIND ABOUT BASKETBALL!
THE END

The team

Jack Charlton's appointment as manager of the Republic of Ireland in 1986 was not met with total approval in the Emerald Isle.

His Sheffield Wednesday, Middlesbrough and Newcastle sides did not enjoy a reputation for open, attacking football but Charlton was not going to change his beliefs for anyone . . . not even the Irish.

He introduced a more direct style, which was not popular at first. But Jack wanted to make the most of the strengths of the English First Division, where most of his players came from. Charlton felt that getting the ball upfield as quickly as possible, into the opponents' "danger area" was the best way to play.

Charlton still has his critics, but he has led Ireland to unprecedented success. They qualified for a major finals for the first time when they reached the 1988 European Championship and in West Germany the Republic won the respect of everyone.

While Bobby Robson's England returned home to a mountain of criticism, Charlton was made an honorary Irishman by the Irish Prime Minister in an emotional scene at Dublin Airport.

Charlton, who helped England win the 1966 World Cup, is now called a footballing genius by the Irish. He's been offered a contract for life and has got Irish eyes smiling after the way the side has progressed over the past three years.

Here are some of the players who have shared in the Republic's recent success. . . .

FAR LEFT
Leeds' tenacious midfielder John Sheridan.
ABOVE
Ray Houghton (centre) is congratulated after scoring the winner against England in the European Championship.
BELOW
Pat Bonner is now rated amongst Europe's top goalkeepers.

that ☘ JACK BUILT

ABOVE
Jack Charlton issues another instruction to his team during a game.

ABOVE
Celtic's Chris Morris . . . Ireland's dependable right-back.
RIGHT
David Kelly opted to play for the Republic rather than England.

Tart Ter

Paul Mason, the young Aberdeen player, shows his skills against Dutch club Feyenoord during a pre-season tournament.

Three stars of the Premier Division . . . Fraser Wishart of Motherwell (far left), Dundee's highly-rated Tommy Coyne (left) and Paul Chambers of St Mirren (right). They may be relatively unknown in England but there are many exciting players in Scotland these days who help to make the League so competitive.

an
rors

Scottish football is booming! Attendances are on the increase and fans are being treated to some outstanding football by some of Britain's most talented players.

It's another goal for Rangers' goal-ace Ally McCoist.

ABOVE
Hibernian's John Collins has been the target of many top English clubs.

CONTINUED

Tartan Terrors
CONTINUED

ABOVE
Iain Ferguson of Hearts, who had such an impressive run in the UEFA Cup last season.

LEFT
Paul McStay, the Celtic midfielder, has been Scotland's top player in recent seasons.
RIGHT
Maurice Malpas, Dundee United's captain, is a full-back who loves to attack.

SPOT THE STARS

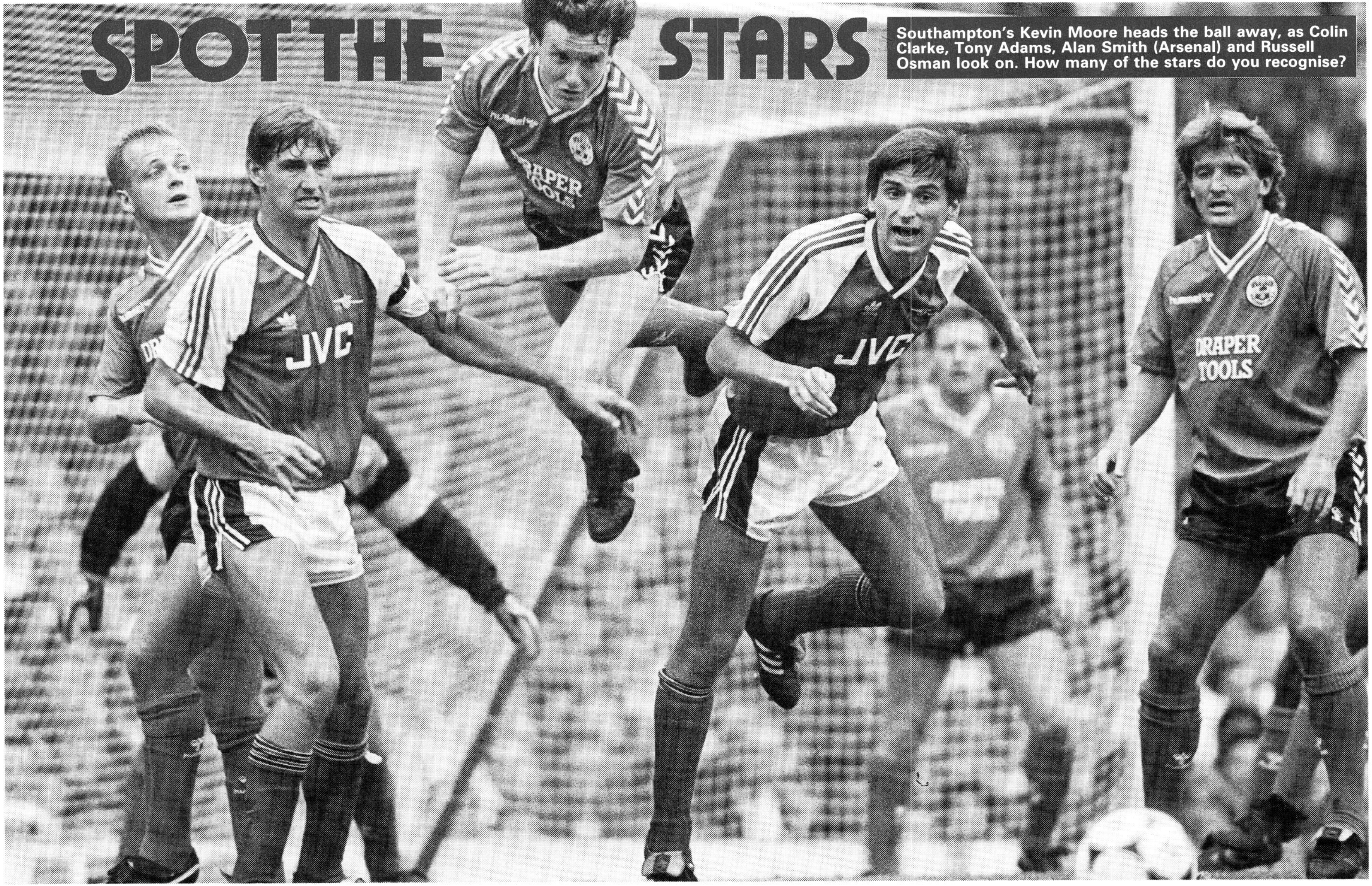

Southampton's Kevin Moore heads the ball away, as Colin Clarke, Tony Adams, Alan Smith (Arsenal) and Russell Osman look on. How many of the stars do you recognise?

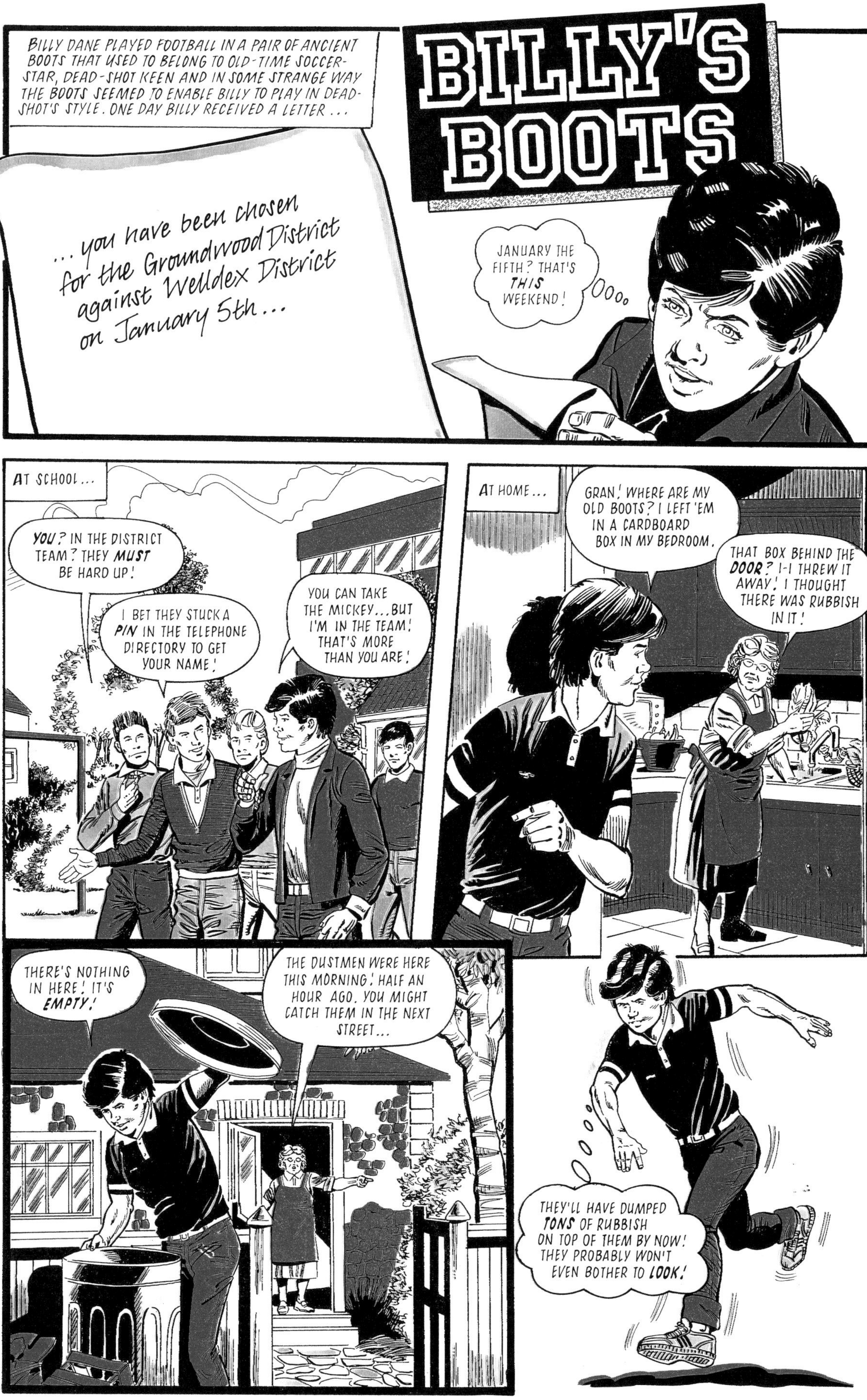

BILLY DANE PLAYED FOOTBALL IN A PAIR OF ANCIENT BOOTS THAT USED TO BELONG TO OLD-TIME SOCCER-STAR, DEAD-SHOT KEEN AND IN SOME STRANGE WAY THE BOOTS SEEMED TO ENABLE BILLY TO PLAY IN DEAD-SHOT'S STYLE. ONE DAY BILLY RECEIVED A LETTER ...

... you have been chosen for the Groundwood District against Welldex District on January 5th ...

AT SCHOOL ...

YOU? IN THE DISTRICT TEAM? THEY MUST BE HARD UP!

I BET THEY STUCK A PIN IN THE TELEPHONE DIRECTORY TO GET YOUR NAME!

YOU CAN TAKE THE MICKEY ... BUT I'M IN THE TEAM! THAT'S MORE THAN YOU ARE!

AT HOME ...

GRAN! WHERE ARE MY OLD BOOTS? I LEFT 'EM IN A CARDBOARD BOX IN MY BEDROOM.

THAT BOX BEHIND THE DOOR? I-I THREW IT AWAY! I THOUGHT THERE WAS RUBBISH IN IT!

THERE'S NOTHING IN HERE! IT'S EMPTY!

THE DUSTMEN WERE HERE THIS MORNING! HALF AN HOUR AGO. YOU MIGHT CATCH THEM IN THE NEXT STREET ...

THEY'LL HAVE DUMPED TONS OF RUBBISH ON TOP OF THEM BY NOW! THEY PROBABLY WON'T EVEN BOTHER TO LOOK!

BUT...
IS THIS THE BOX, SON? IF IT ISN'T, YOU'VE HAD IT! EVERYTHING ELSE IS WELL BURIED!
THAT'S IT! MY SOCCER BOOTS ARE IN IT!
YOU GOT ME RUMMAGING AROUND LOOKING FOR THOSE THINGS? THEY OUGHT TO HAVE BEEN THROWN AWAY YEARS AGO!
THEY'RE SPECIAL! I PLAY IN THEM! THANKS, MISTER! THANKS A LOT! YOU'VE SAVED MY FOOTBALL CAREER!
LATER...
OI, WONDER-BOY! COMING UP THE REC FOR TRAINING? WE'RE JUST GOING.
BE OUT IN A MINUTE! SEE YOU UP THERE!
I'M NOT TAKING THESE UP THE REC! I'LL PACK 'EM READY TO TAKE TO THE DISTRICT MATCH...
ROY
ROVERS
AT THE REC...
I THOUGHT YOU SAID WE WERE TRAINING? THIS IS A MATCH!
ANYONE CAN JOIN IN. IT'LL BE JUST THE JOB FOR YOU ... A LIGHT WORK-OUT BEFORE THAT BIG GAME YOU'RE IN TOMORROW!
IT'S JUST A KICK-ABOUT!
COME ON, DANE... CHASE IT! YOU'RE SUPPOSED TO BE A GOOD PLAYER!
I'D HAVE BROUGHT THE OLD BOOTS IF I'D KNOWN WE WERE PLAYING A GAME! I'LL BE USELESS IN THESE TRAINERS...

WHAT'S THAT SUPPOSED TO BE! YOU CAN GO AND GET IT!
YOU'RE ABOUT AS GOOD AS MY LITTLE SISTER! SHE CAN'T KICK STRAIGHT, EITHER!
DUNNO HOW YOU GOT IN THE DISTRICT TEAM, MATE! YOU CAN'T SHOOT!
THE CROWD WON'T HALF GET AFTER YOU IF YOU DO THAT ON SATURDAY!
ANYONE CAN MISS! IT'S ONLY PRACTICE, ANYWAY!
ON SATURDAY MORNING...
DO I HAVE TO TAKE ALL THIS STUFF, GRAN?
YES! IT MIGHT RAIN. AND I'VE PACKED SOME SANDWICHES. YOU'LL BE GLAD OF THEM AFTER THE GAME.
THE GROUND WAS A TRAIN RIDE AWAY...
WONDER WHY I WAS PICKED FOR THE DISTRICT TEAM? THEY MUST HAVE SEEN ME PLAY FOR GROUND-WOOD SCHOOL! IF I DO WELL, I MIGHT EVEN GET PICKED FOR THE COUNTY SIDE!
THERE COULD BE SCOUTS FROM PROFESSIONAL CLUBS THERE, TOO! THEY COULD BE WATCHING... AND SPOT ME! GET ME A TRIAL WITH A THIRD OR FOURTH DIVISION CLUB!
TINSDALE STATION! ANYONE FOR TINSDALE? HURRY ALONG!
OH, CRUMBS! THAT'S ME! I GET OFF HERE...
THEN...
TINSDALE
I'VE LEFT MY HOLD-ALL ON THE TRAIN!
THEY'LL FIND IT AT BENSFORD STATION... AT THE END OF THE LINE! YOU CAN COLLECT IT THERE.

I'M PLAYING FOOTBALL AT THREE O'CLOCK. ALL MY GEAR'S IN THE HOLD-ALL. I'VE GOT TO HAVE IT!
YOU COULD GET THE BUS TO BENSFORD. SHOULD BE TIME TO GET THERE AND BACK. IT'LL BE TIGHT, THOUGH!
AT BENSFORD STATION...
OFFICE
LOST PROPERTY
IT'S NOT BEEN HANDED IN YET! YOU'LL HAVE TO WAIT UNTIL THEY'VE FINISHED CLEANING THE CARRIAGES.
MY GAME KICKS OFF IN HALF-AN-HOUR! I'LL BE LATE!
TEN MINUTES LATER...
HERE IT IS!
I'M GOING OFF DUTY NOW. I'LL GIVE YOU A LIFT BACK TO TINSDALE, IF YOU LIKE! I'VE GOT A MOTORBIKE.
THANKS, MISTER THE BUS'LL NEVER GET ME THERE IN TIME.
PUT THAT ON. ALWAYS CARRY A SPARE FOR PASSENGERS!
HOPE HE GETS A SHIFT ON. IT'S NEARLY TWENTY-TO-THREE!
BILLY ARRIVED JUST BEFORE THE KICK-OFF...
ONE MORE MINUTE AND YOU'D HAVE LOST YOUR CHANCE, SON! GET CHANGED. EVERY-ONE ELSE IS OUT THERE.
SORRY SIR! I LEFT MY FOOTBALL GEAR ON THE TRAIN.
TEN MINUTES LATER...
WAKE UP, GROUNDWOOD!
YOU'LL HAVE TO MOVE FASTER THAN THAT!
THAT'S ME THE'RE HAVING A GO AT!

THEN...
DON'T PASS IT TO THEM!
COULDN'T HELP IT! DIDN'T KICK IT HARD ENOUGH! DEAD-SHOT'S OLD BOOTS DON'T SEEM TO BE DOING MUCH FOR ME!
JUST BEFORE HALF-TIME...
GOOD SAVE!
YOU'RE SUPPOSED TO BEAT HIM, SON... NOT GIVE HIM GOALKEEPING PRACTICE!
IT WASN'T A BAD SHOT! I GOT IT ON TARGET!
SECOND HALF...
I HAVEN'T HAD A KICK THIS HALF! ALL THE PLAY'S BEEN DOWN OUR END! WE'LL GET WHACKED IF WE DON'T WATCH IT!
THEN GROUNDWOOD DISTRICT BROKE AWAY...
GROUNDWOOD! GROUNDWOOD! GROUNDWOOD!
THE CROWD ARE GETTING BEHIND US! AND DEAD-SHOT'S OLD BOOTS ARE MAKING ME RUN! SOMETHING'S GOING TO HAPPEN!
GOOD CROSS!
NO-ONE THERE TO GET ON THE END OF IT, THOUGH!
IT'S GOING TO CLEAR THEM. IT'S COMING RIGHT OVER THEIR HEADS!

YESSSS! IT'S THERE! GREAT HEADER!
WHY WASN'T HE CLOSED DOWN?
DIDN'T KNOW HE WAS THERE, DID WE!
THIS IS WHY THE OLD BOOTS MADE ME RUN! TO GET ME IN POSITION!
THAT EVENING...
YOU ATE YOUR SANDWICHES, I HOPE? AND I SEE THAT RAIN-COAT CAME IN USEFUL. HOW DID YOU GET ON AT FOOTBALL?
WE WON, GRAN! ONE-NIL. AND I SCORED THE ONLY GOAL... WITH A SMASHING HEADER!
YOU DON'T WEAR FOOTBALL BOOTS ON YOUR HEAD! I DON'T KNOW WHY YOU MADE ALL THAT FUSS ABOUT GETTING THEM BACK FROM THE DUSTMAN! YOU'D HAVE SCORED JUST AS WELL WITHOUT THEM!
YOU DON'T UNDERSTAND, GRAN! THE BOOTS RAN ME INTO THE RIGHT PLACE TO HEAD THE BALL!
ME AND DEAD-SHOT KEEN PLAY IN THE SAME STYLE, SEE! HIS OLD BOOTS DO SOMETHING FOR ME!
DO THEY? WELL, I'LL BELIEVE YOU... THOUSANDS WOULDN'T!
I DON'T SUPPOSE ANY PROFESSIONAL SCOUTS WILL BE AFTER ME! BUT I STILL DON'T WANT THE OLD BOOTS TO BE THROWN AWAY!
THAT SHOULD KEEP 'EM SAFE!
Valuable. Do not throw away!
The End

MARA

The greatest footballer in the world

Maradona in action for Napoli . . . here he comes away from Verona's West German star Hans-Peter Briegel.

DONA

Diego Armando Maradona, the greatest footballer in the world, has cost a staggering £8 million during his career . . . and has probably earned himself even more.

Maradona led Argentina to World Cup victory in 1986 when they beat West Germany 3–2 in an exciting final in Mèxico City.

Yet the superstar comes from a humble background and was born in Lanus, a suburb of Buenos Aires, the capital of Argentina.

He was discovered playing for a team called Los Cebollitos – the Little Onions. He signed for Argentinos Juniors, one of the less fashionable clubs of Buenos Aires. In fact, Argentinos Juniors were so impressed by the Little Onions that they signed the entire team and turned them into one of the club's official youth sides!

He made his First Division debut aged 16 and was an instant hit. A few months later he won his first cap for Argentina against Hungary but after much thought Cesar Menotti left Maradona out of his squad for the 1978 World Cup which the South Americans won.

UPSET

Maradona was so upset at being omitted that he did not talk to Menotti for six months!

They eventually buried the hatchet and Maradona led his country to success in the World Youth Cup in 1979.

Boca Juniors, one of Argentina's biggest clubs, paid £1 million for Maradona and he inspired them to the Championship in 1981.

Maradona made his debut in the World Cup finals in Spain in 1982 but could not help them to retain their crown. In fact, the tournament was a personal disaster for Maradona who was sent-off for kicking Brazil's Batista.

Straight after the 1982 World Cup he joined Barcelona for £2 million but his stay in Spain was hit by illness and injury. Terry Venables sold Maradona

CONTINUED

MARADONA

CONTINUED

to Napoli for £5 million in 1984 and two years later the Argentine achieved his ambition of captaining his country to their World Cup triumph.

He has also won the Italian Championship with Napoli and Maradona is idolised in his adopted Italian home.

Maradona earns around £1 million from his football activities each year. He is on a percentage of the gate when Napoli play friendlies while the little Argentine collects huge sums from other games.

For instance, he was paid £100,000 to play for the Rest of the World XI against the Football League in the Centenary game at Wembley.

He has many commercial interests and it is probably true to say no player in the history of football has earned more from the sport.

HANDBALL

Perhaps the only blot on Maradona's glorious career is the infamous 'handball' goal he scored against England in Mexico. It seemed like everyone except the match officials saw Maradona punch the ball over Peter Shilton – he called it the Hand of God.

The action attracted incredible attention from the British media. Television ran and re-ran the incident countless times, and newspapers still refer to it.

That one, possibly impulsive, action should not however disguise the pure genius of the little man from Argentina.

ABOVE
Football League XI versus Rest of the World, Wembley, 1987 . . . Maradona shakes hands with Bryan Robson.
BELOW
Younger brother Hugo leads the way during training with Argentina's youth team.

His second goal in the match – which Argentina won by two goals to one – was a magnificent individual effort. He went on an amazing sixty-yard run, weaving in and out of England players as though they were hardly there, and slid the ball past Peter Shilton.

It showed the world that when Diego Maradona uses his feet, there is no-one like him. He is incomparable.

Next year, Maradona will lead Argentina in their defence of the World Cup in Italy. Who would bet against the little man who began his career with the Little Onions being the star of the 1990 World Cup, too?

The NEW ROY RACE

The capacity crowd crammed into Mel Park stadium was watching a display of First Division football magic. Roars of excitement and approval thundered from fifty thousand throats as the home team Melchester Rovers swept time and again into their opponents' half; finding space, working together as a single unit and swinging the ball from man to man with pinpoint accuracy.

Rovers' skipper and player-manager Roy Race had never been in finer form. He seemed to be everywhere at once; helping in defence, tackling in midfield, spearheading the attack up front, covering every metre of the pitch with skill and tireless energy. Sports commentators had said that this Fourth Round F.A. Cup-Tie against Stamford City would be a hard-fought, hard-tackling match with few goals and a result that could go either way. Instead, Roy Race and his men had mixed their own special brand of 'Melchester Magic' and turned the game into a one-sided walkover!

Attacking from the very first blast of the whistle, Rovers were a goal up in four and a half minutes, a dazzling solo effort by Vietnamese winger Pak Soon, who raced from the halfway line to swerve past three City defenders and hit a low, hard shot into the back of the net past the advancing 'keeper. Two more goals followed before half-time, both scored by 'The King' himself, Roy Race! One was a low, diving header from a Blackie Gray cross, the other a perfectly-timed volley from the edge of the box that was bulging the back of the net before the demoralised Stamford defence even knew what was happening.

Now it was well into the second half, and urged on by their screaming, goal-hungry fans, the Melchester machine was once again on the move, probing deep into their opponents' half with effortless skill and speed. Led by 'Hard Man' Johnny Dexter, Rovers' back four joined the attack with a series of short, sharp, scything passes that tore City's defensive wall to pieces.

"Attaboy, Johnny," yelled Roy. "Keep coming! Make more ground."

The Hard Man grinned. Gaining speed, he powered his way to the edge of the penalty area, jinked past a desperate sliding tackle and then chipped the ball back through a yawning gap to where the Melchester skipper was running all by himself into acres of space. Roy had all the time in the world. He flicked the ball from his right foot to his left, and unleashed what the entire footballing public had come to know as . . . *"Racey's Rocket"!* City's goalkeeper didn't even see the ball, let alone attempt to save it. Rovers were four–nil up, Roy Race had scored a hat-trick, and the explosion of sound from Mel Park stadium could be heard two miles away at the city rail terminus.

High in the deafening babble of the south stand, an old man sat alone. The passing years had hunched his shoulders and sharpened the bones of his face. Only his eyes still glowed with life. They were dark brown, alert and bright. As bright as a bird's. "Pure poetry in motion," said the old man to himself, "that's Roy Race. He knows more ways to beat a player than anybody I've ever seen. History will probably put him down as one of the greatest footballers of all time . . . and maybe in a way it's partly thanks to me, who knows?" Smiling, the old man rose and pushed his way slowly through the cheering crowd towards one of the aisles.

As the final whistle blew, Roy Race was carried shoulder-high from the pitch by his triumphant team-mates. In Rovers' dressing-room there were scenes of wild and happy chaos. Players were shouting in each other's ears, reliving every goal, every moment of the game. General manager Ben Galloway had opened a bottle of champagne and was spraying it recklessly round the room. Duncan McKay and Rob Richards were already in the team bath – with their boots still on. Players and officials alike were literally blowing off steam after the tension, drama and hard work of the past ninety minutes.

Suddenly Roy became aware of raised voices shouting outside the locked dressing-room door.

"Beat it, Pops, will you? The public ain't allowed down here, it's *private*!"

"I've told you a dozen times, I want to see Roy Race!"

"That makes you and fifty thousand others! Now *beat it*, will ya?"

"No, damn you, this is *important*!"

Roy unlocked the door, yanked it open and stuck his head out. In the dimness of the corridor, two club security men were struggling with someone. "Who is it?" asked Roy. "Some stray autograph hunter who won't take no for an answer?"

"Naw, this geezer looks as if he's escaped from an Old Folks' Home! Must be seventy-five if he's a day! Caught him strolling through the staff entrance cool as an ice cube and demanding to see you. Says his name is Alf Dunsfeld or Dunsfield or something . . ."

"Alf *Dunsford*?" Roy was across the passage in a single bound, pulling the two security men apart, a grin splitting his sweat-stained features from ear to ear. "Alf! It *is* you, by heck! *Alf Dunsford*!"

"Hello, lad," said the old man, watching his thin, blue-veined fingers being swallowed up in Roy's eager, double-handed grasp of friendship. "It would have been easier to 'phone and make an appointment, but I reckoned the news I have for you couldn't wait, and besides, I wanted to see the cup-tie." Alf's bird-bright eyes twinkled with pleasure. "Good win out there today, lad. You're sharper than ever!"

"Thanks, Alf. Coming from you, that really *means* something."

One of the security guards coughed discreetly. "So it's -er-all right if this gent stays here with you, Mr Race, yes?"

"You bet your sweet life it is," said Roy. "Alf Dunsford has the finest football brain in this country or any other. He's also the best talent scout who ever trod a touchline. He's discovered more soccer stars than any other man I know. He also," added Roy quietly, "was the first man to spot *me*! Remember, Alf . . . all those years ago?"

"I remember like it were yesterday," said Dunsford wistfully. "A sniffy little kid with a flour-and-paste complexion and legs like twigs playing for the Melchester Under-Elevens. Roy Race they said his name was. Looked like he'd been brought up on a diet of bread and dripping. 'One puff of wind and he'll end up on the next pitch,' I thought. Ten minutes into the game I knew I'd discovered a genius," said Alf with a grin. "That runny-nosed Roy Race was gifted with more footballing ability than any kid I'd ever seen. I put him in touch with the right people, and . . . well, the rest is history."

Roy grinned and led his old friend towards the dressing-room. "We've got a lot to talk about, Alf," he said, "but let me have a shower, get changed and I'll see you in half an hour."

In a quiet café not far from the ground, the two men faced each other over steaming mugs of tea. "Okay, now tell me the news that couldn't wait," said Roy.

"Last Saturday afternoon I saw a fourteen-year-old kid playing football," said Alf quietly. "His name is Danny Clarke and he lives up in Charnford. He's built like a stick of rhubarb but moves like a greyhound. Watching him was like watching you all those years ago. Poetry in motion. A potential genius." Alf paused and stared hard over the rim of his cup. "I never thought it would ever happen again," he added softly, "but I think I've found another Roy Race."

The Melchester skipper felt a growing sense of excitement. Praise from Alf Dunsford was praise indeed, and the finding and signing of promising young players was a vital part of every football manager's job. "Okay, we'll go and have a look at him," said Roy. "When is this kid playing again?"

"Wednesday morning," said Alf promptly. "An under-fifteens schools' match. And I hope it ain't blooming well raining. My bones are getting too old to watch football in the rain."

There was no rain, there was sleet instead! The coal-mining town of Charnford was bleak at the best of times; today it was positively dismal. But for Roy and Alf Dunsford, the cold and discomfort soon became minor irritations as they warmed to the pure delight of watching fourteen-year-old Danny Clarke destroy the opposing school team practically single-handed. Charnford won by five goals to one, all scored by the thin, darting, dynamic youngster.

"You're right, Alf," said Roy softly. "He *is* the spitting image of me all those years ago. I've seen all I want to see. We'll talk to Danny Clarke about signing on as an apprentice for Melchester Rovers, then visit his parents and hope to get their approval."

"That," said Alf glumly, "is where we might run into a problem. I haven't told you before, but Danny's real parents are dead. He lives with his step-father now, and two step-brothers. The three of them are out of work coal miners, and to put it mildly, Roy . . . they're not nice people to know!"

Roy found out exactly what the old scout meant as soon as he stepped through the front door of the crumbling terraced house which had been built a hundred and fifty years before in the shadow of a slag heap close to the Charnford mine. Danny Clarke's step-father was called Bert Sagger, a surly, heavy-jowled man in his mid-fifties, dressed in a grease-stained pullover and shapeless trousers. He was lying slumped in an armchair when Roy and Alf came in, his heavy stomach heaving flabbily when he coughed . . . which was often. Bert's two sons, Jerry and Fred, were also there, silent, sullen replicas of their father. The whole room stank of unwashed bodies, unwashed clothes and unwashed dishes.

Young Danny ushered his two visitors forward. The boy was even paler than normal, tense and almost trembling with excitement. The thought of being able to sign as an apprentice for Melchester Rovers was almost more than he could bear.

"I guess Danny's told you we'd like him with us at the club," said Roy pleasantly. "If he turns out to be as good as I think he is, your step-son has a great future ahead of him."

"Glad to hear it," growled Bert Sagger. "At least it means somebody *else* will be feeding and looking after the brat from now on."

"Some *home-life* the poor kid's got here," thought Roy angrily, then forced himself to speak pleasantly once again: "Okay, then I take it that as Danny's legal guardian you have no objection to him signing apprentice forms for Melchester Rovers, right?"

"I didn't say that, Mister!" Suddenly there was a mean, crafty gleam in Bert Sagger's eyes. He sat up and gave Roy a knowing wink. "If I agreed to let Danny sign, I guess there would something in it for me too, eh?"

"What are you talking about?" asked Roy.

"Don't come the innocent with me, Racey! You know as well as I do that when promising kids are snapped up by big clubs, the parents suddenly find themselves driving a new car, or taking a holiday in the Bahamas, or opening a savings account with a nice few quid in it, all done quietly with no fuss, just a friendly gentlemen's agreement, know what I mean?"

"If you're asking for a *bribe*, Sagger, forget it! The Melchester Rovers Football Club has never made an illegal payment in its life and it isn't going to start now."

"Okay," said Sagger with a leer. "No sweetener, no signature. If Danny's as good as you say, maybe some other club that ain't so *fussy* will want him on their books."

"B-but Melchester's the best club in the whole country," cried Danny, coming forward with tears in his eyes. "I'd *never* want to play for anybody else."

"Shut up, kid, as your legal guardian, *I'm* the one who'll decide your future." Sagger heaved himself to his feet and stared Roy right in the eye. "End of conversation, Mister. Why not go back to Mel Park and think about it?"

"I don't have to," said Roy bitterly. "The only one I'm sorry for in this house is young Danny Clarke." Beckoning the boy forward, he led him into the tiny hall between the sitting-room and the front door. "Don't give up hope, Danny," he said, "maybe I'll find a way out of this mess for you. Here –" from his inside pocket, Roy withdrew two stand tickets for Rovers' next home game, and one of his neatly-printed visiting cards. "Use these tickets to watch us play our next league match against Burndean. Bring a mate with you and have a day out. My visiting card has my club address and 'phone number on it. If you ever run into trouble with Sagger or your step-brothers, give me a ring right away, right?"

"Okay, Mr Race," said Danny tearfully, "and thanks for what you tried to do tonight. Thanks a million."

For Alf and Roy it was a dismal journey home that evening. Both men knew that they had probably seen the last of Danny Clarke's talent as far as Melchester Rovers was concerned. Another, more unscrupulous club was bound to end up lining Bert Sagger's pockets for the privilege of the youngster's signature on a piece of paper.

But there was more to the running of a football club than the signing of one fourteen-year-old schoolboy! In the days that followed, Roy had a lot of managerial paperwork to do in addition to picking the team for the vital league match against Burndean, who were lying fourth in the table, one point ahead of Melchester Rovers.

Roy had decided to change his team tactics against Burndean. After the sparkling four–nil win against Stamford City and his own brilliant hat-trick, Roy knew he'd be more heavily marked than usual in an effort to blot him out of the game. So he decided to pull himself back from his normal role as frontline striker and play deep in midfield, hoping that he would confuse and puzzle the Burndean defenders who had been ordered to stay with him at all costs.

The plan worked brilliantly. As two burly Burndean 'hard men' shadowed Roy's every step, waiting for a burst of speed and a "Racey's Rocket" that never came, Steve Wootten and Duncan McKay used their power and speed as overlapping full-backs to launch a series of attacks up both wings and give Rovers a two to one advantage in Burndean's penalty area. From one such run, Wootten pulled the ball back sharply for Rob Richards to shoot. It was cleared but picked up by Danish international Olly Olsen who shot on the run from thirty metres out to send the ball searing into the net for a brilliantly-taken goal. Just before half-time, Blackie Gray was brought down in the penalty area and Roy himself had the pleasure of thumping the ball into the net for a two-goal lead.

As Rovers trooped off for the break, Roy caught a glimpse of two familiar figures high in the stand near the directors' box. They waved, shouted and clapped. Roy stared in amazement. One of the figures was Danny Clarke, the other his step-father, Bert Sagger. Danny hadn't given his spare free ticket to a friend, but to his surly guardian. Only this time, Sagger wasn't so surly. He was grinning from ear to ear, revealing a mouthful of yellow, nicotine-stained teeth. Danny was smiling too, and chatting with his step-father as though they were and always had been, the very best of friends. "What the *heck* is going on?" thought Roy in amazement.

He found out as soon as the match was over, another victory for Rovers by three goals to one. Alf Dunsford himself brought Danny and Bert Sagger down to Roy's office to explain. The ex-miner was friendliness itself. "After you left the other day I realised how wrong I'd been," he said humbly. "Danny's career comes first, and if the lad wants to sign for Melchester Rovers, I'm damned if I'll be the one to stand in his way."

"Isn't that the *greatest news ever*, Mr Race?" yelled Danny.

"Well, yes . . . yes, it's fantastic," said Roy. He looked once again at Bert Sagger. The man was still smiling broadly, but his eyes were dead and expressionless. Something was going on . . . but *what*? "And about the - uhm-holiday in the Bahamas you mentioned before, Sagger?"

"Forget I even asked for it, Mister. Stupid of me. I should have known better and that's a fact."

"Okay," said Roy, "let's arrange a date next week for the official signing. Wednesday morning, maybe. You come along with young Danny, and I'll set things up."

"Champion," beamed Bert Sagger, slapping his step-son's shoulder. "Next Wednesday it is."

At ten o'clock that night as Roy Race was watching television at home, his wife Penny answered a heavy knock at the front door. She returned a few moments later with a tall, well-built, curly-haired stranger at her side. "This is Detective-Inspector John Page of Melchester C.I.D., Roy," she said nervously. "He wants to ask you a few questions about somebody called . . ."

"Bert Sagger, Mr Race. I believe you know him, is that right?"

"Yes," said Roy, startled. "I'm hoping to sign his stepson next week as a club apprentice. Why?"

"We've had our eye on Bert Sagger and his two sons for some time," said the Inspector. "We know they're villains, only we can't prove it. Two days ago, a department store in Charnford was robbed. Among various items of property that were stolen a considerable sum of money in cash. Five thousand pounds, to be exact. The staff payroll. Acting on information received, we searched Sagger's house and found a large brown envelope containing that sum in used notes."

"Then you've got your proof, right?"

"Wrong," said the policeman. "Also in that brown envelope was a small business card. A visiting card. *Your* visiting card, Mr Race." Slowly, Page extended his hand and Roy found himself staring at it.

"I gave that card to young Danny Clarke, the schoolboy I want to sign," said Roy weakly. "Why the heck did it end up in an envelope full of stolen money?"

"Because Bert Sagger and his sons swear that the money *wasn't* stolen, Mr Race. They swear that the five thousand pounds was given to them by *you*, as an inducement to make sure that young Danny Clarke signed for Melchester Rovers and no other club."

Roy sat down. Suddenly the whole sordid affair had become crystal clear. In extreme danger of being nicked by the law, Bert Sagger and his sons had seized on Roy's visit as the perfect excuse.

"*Did* you give the Saggers that money, Mr Race?"

"No," said Roy firmly, "I didn't give them a penny . . . only how the heck am I going to *prove* it?"

"Exactly," said the Inspector. "That's what the Saggers are banking on. It's their word against yours, and until we have definite proof one way or the other, no court in the land would ever convict them."

"Which is why Bert Sagger was suddenly all sweetness and light at the game today," said Roy bitterly. "I realise now why he agreed so easily to let Danny sign on. He had me over a barrel and I didn't even know it."

"There's something else you don't know yet, Mr Race," said Page sadly. "To make his story of the five thousand pound bribe even *bigger* news, Bert Sagger blabbed to the local press. I'm afraid you and Melchester Rovers will be making headlines by Monday morning at the latest."

"Oh, no," groaned Roy. "Not that. Not the *newspapers*, too!"

If Roy had hoped for a miracle, it didn't happen. The early edition headlines were big, bold and more than a little bruising. 'ROY RACE IN SCHOOLBOY BRIBE SCANDAL', blared one. 'ROVERS' BACKHANDER BOMBSHELL', screamed another. 'GOLDEN BOY, GOLDEN HAND-

SHAKE', said a third.

First thing on Monday morning, Roy was hauled before the Melchester board of directors and told in no uncertain fashion that when Bert Sagger and Danny Clarke arrived at the club on Wednesday, the whole truth concerning the 'bribe' had to be thrashed out once and for all. Old Alf Dunsford was sympathy itself. He met Roy later and promised his full support. "I was there too, remember. I can swear to the directors and the press that no money ever changed hands."

"Thanks, Alf, but that won't change anything. It's still our word against the Saggers. Until some *real* proof turns up, we're just bashing our heads against a brick wall."

"Then what are you going to do?" asked Alf.

"Try something pretty desperate," said Roy grimly. "I'm going to have another word with Detective-Inspector Page and then talk to the first team squad. If what I've got in mind doesn't work, then the *next* headline will be . . . ROY RACE RESIGNS!"

Bert Sagger and Danny Clarke arrived promptly for their appointment on the Wednesday morning. The youngster was puzzled and worried by all the talk about money changing hands. He knew he hadn't *seen* Roy give a bulging brown envelope to his step-father, but Bert had told him angrily and bluntly that he had, and the boy was too scared of his guardian to argue. He'd been told to keep his mouth shut if he wanted to play football for Melchester Rovers, and he intended to do just that.

Old Alf Dunsford led the two of them into the boardroom and made the necessary introductions. The chairman frowned. "Where's the manager?" he asked irritably. "Where's Roy Race?"

"He'll be along later," said Alf mildly. "He told me to tell you that he'd gone out for a training run with the first team squad this morning."

"A *training run*? Today of all days?" The chairman's face was changing colour from red to white and then back again. "Doesn't Race know that practically every news reporter in Britain is waiting outside for the result of this meeting? How *dare* he vanish into thin air!"

"He won't be too long, sir, I'm sure of it," said Alf with a confidence he certainly didn't feel.

An hour later there was a roar of disbelief from the throng of reporters gathered outside the players' entrance to the Mel Park stadium. Trotting fast along the road towards the ground, wearing tracksuits and trainers, were the Melchester Rovers' first team squad and their skipper Roy Race. Two police cars brought up the rear, in one of which sat the grim-faced figure of Detective-Inspector John Page, and the sulky, sullen figures of Fred and Jerry Sagger.

As the noise rose to a level approaching pandemonium, Bert Sagger, Danny Clarke, the entire Melchester board of directors and Alf Dunsford, all hurried downstairs to find out what was going on. They were confronted by the grinning, bulky shape of Roy Race shrugging off two mink coats and a silk evening cape which had been draped round his shoulders. Under each arm, Roy also carried a couple of radio-cassette recorders, a video camera. Bruno Johnson was lugging a compact disc recorder on his broad shoulders.

"All over, Bert," said Roy cheerfully, slapping the ex-miner on the back. "You're *nicked*, mate. All this gear was stolen from the department store at the same time as that five thousand quid. Inspector Page has all the proof he needs now."

"How . . .?" said Bert weakly, and then stopped.

"Easy," said Roy. "First I asked the police if they'd recovered the other property that was stolen at the same time as the money. They said no, so I "*persuaded*" the first team lads to go for a jog with me over Charnford way. It so happened that we found ourselves outside the Saggers' house at about eleven o'clock. Bruno Johnson suggested that we should invite ourselves in for a cup of tea. We found Fred and Jerry Sagger lolling about in the sitting-room. Then 'Hard-Man' Johnny Dexter asked

them politely if they knew anything about a robbery and stolen goods and things like that. You did ask them *politely*, didn't you, Johnny?"

"Yeah, all I had to do was shove my ugly mug close to theirs and they started to sing like little yellow canaries! Next thing we know, they're leading us outside and showing us all sorts of things like mink coats, radios and cameras hidden in the slag heap at the back. They even wrote us a lovely letter saying how they stole five grand from the store too, and tried to say how it came from Roy Race."

"You stupid, chicken-hearted, blabbering berks!" Bert Sagger was suddenly rushing at his sons, fists clenched and swinging like gnarled clubs. He didn't get two yards before he was stopped and held fast by two burly uniformed policeman.

Smiling, Roy Race bent over the trembling figure of young Danny Clarke. "It's all over now, son," he said gently. "Your step-father's no good and never has been. Once his trial's over, we'll make sure the courts take away his power of legal guardianship. My wife Penny will look after you until you're old enough to move into club digs."

"Th-then I really *will* be signing for Melchester Rovers?" asked Danny in a small hushed voice.

"You *bet* you will," said the King of Mel Park. "Now let's go inside and have a long talk . . . about football!"

Watching them go, old Alf Dunsford had a strange, almost dream-like expression on his face. "To find *one* Roy Race in a lifetime is amazing enough," he said to himself. "To find *two*, is little short of a miracle!"

THE END

ACTION E·X·T·R·A

GEORGE LAWRENCE
(Millwall)

A speedy, skilful winger with an eye for goal, Lawrence made only 10 League appearances for Southampton before joining Oxford. He returned to the Dell in 1985 but two years later signed for Millwall in a £65,000 deal and helped the London club to win promotion to Division One.

DANGER MEN!

TONY COTTEE
(Everton)

Tony Cottee could hardly have had a better start to his career with Everton . . . the former West Ham striker scored a hat-trick against Newcastle at Goodison Park following his £2 million transfer in the summer of 1988. And he's not stopped scoring since!

DANGER MEN!

FRANK McAVENNIE (Celtic)

Frank McAvennie quickly proved himself in English football with West Ham after joining them for £400,000. He then returned to Scotland in a £1 million deal and helped Celtic to win the League and Cup "double".

DANGER MEN!

PAUL STEWART (Spurs)

Some people claimed that Paul Stewart wasn't worth the £1.7 million Tottenham paid Manchester City but the pacey striker soon proved them wrong with some spectacular goals for the London club. After a poor start, Spurs finally got into their stride, helped by the ex-Manchester man.

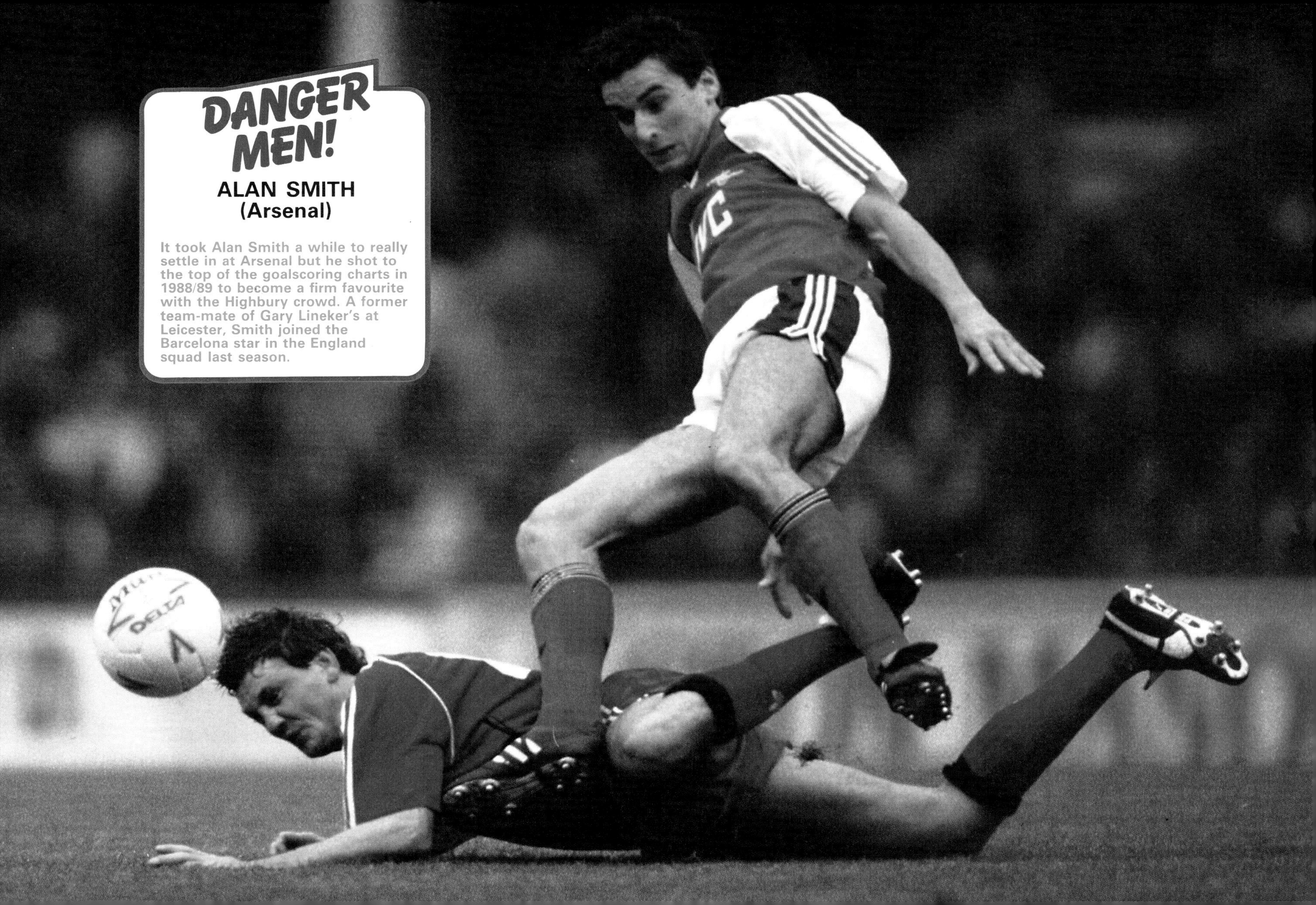

DANGER MEN!

ALAN SMITH (Arsenal)

It took Alan Smith a while to really settle in at Arsenal but he shot to the top of the goalscoring charts in 1988/89 to become a firm favourite with the Highbury crowd. A former team-mate of Gary Lineker's at Leicester, Smith joined the Barcelona star in the England squad last season.

DANGER MEN!

PAUL GODDARD (Derby)

Began his career with QPR before moving across London to West Ham. Goddard then joined Newcastle in 1986 before choosing Derby in preference to Liverpool two years later. He has won one full England cap to date, but there could be more in the pipeline.

DANGER MEN!

ALLY McCOIST (Rangers)

Started his career with St. Johnstone before joining Sunderland. He never found his best form at Roker Park but since joining Rangers in 1983 he has become Scotland's top goalscorer and a hero at Ibrox Park. On his day, he's a real danger man.

DANGER MEN!

ROBERT FLECK
(Norwich)

After "learning his trade" with Partick Thistle, Fleck moved to Rangers before joining Norwich for £400,000 in December, 1987. His dynamic style was a feature of Norwich's impressive form in 1988/89, which took the rest of football by surprise.

DANGER MEN!

MICK HARFORD (Luton)

Mick Harford is one of the most effective target men in English football, his height and power a problem for even the strongest defenders. Has played for Lincoln, Newcastle, Bristol City and Birmingham as well as Luton . . . and England.

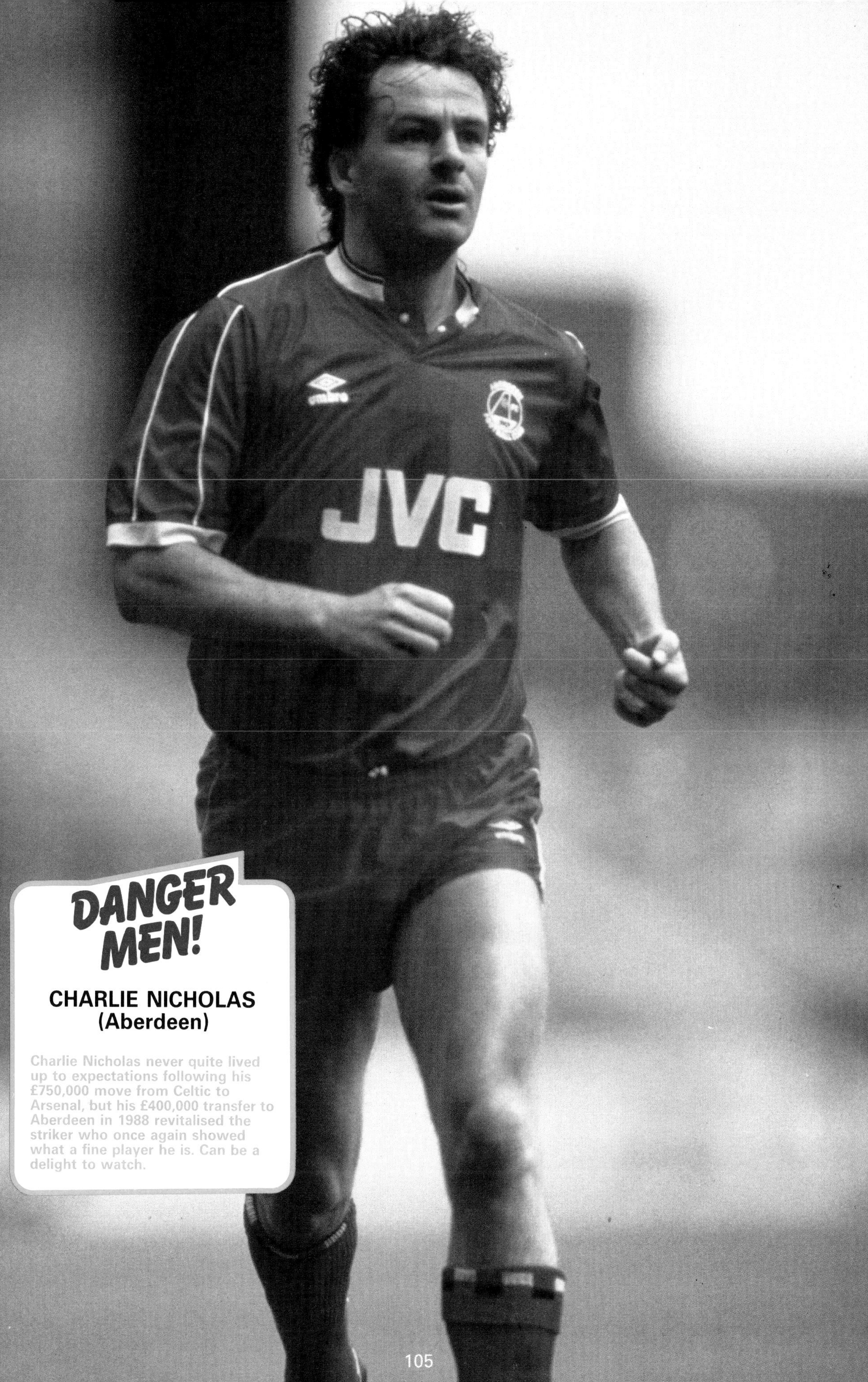

DANGER MEN!

CHARLIE NICHOLAS
(Aberdeen)

Charlie Nicholas never quite lived up to expectations following his £750,000 move from Celtic to Arsenal, but his £400,000 transfer to Aberdeen in 1988 revitalised the striker who once again showed what a fine player he is. Can be a delight to watch.

DANGER MEN!

TONY CASCARINO
(Millwall)

Considering his success with Millwall after his £200,000 transfer in 1987, it is surprising he didn't join a bigger club before. He signed for Gillingham in 1982 from Crokenhill – the "fee" was a set of track-suits! Now a regular with the Republic of Ireland.

DANGER MEN!

MIRANDINHA (Newcastle)

Francisco Da Silva, better known as Mirandinha, became the first Brazilian to sign for a Football League club when he joined Newcastle in 1987 from Palmeiras for £600,000. His ball trickery and goalscoring talents have been a welcome addition to English football.

DANGER MEN!

NIGEL CLOUGH (Forest)

Dad Brian calls him "the number nine" and it's a case of like father, like son . . . the Forest manager was also a centre-forward of the highest calibre. It hasn't been easy for Nigel having a famous dad, but "the number nine's" skill has made him a personality in his own right.

DANGER MEN!

JOHN BARNES (Liverpool)

One of the most exciting players in the League, Barnes cost Liverpool £900,000 in 1987 and in his first season won a Championship medal and was named Footballer of the Year. It's a mystery why he hasn't been quite so successful with England.

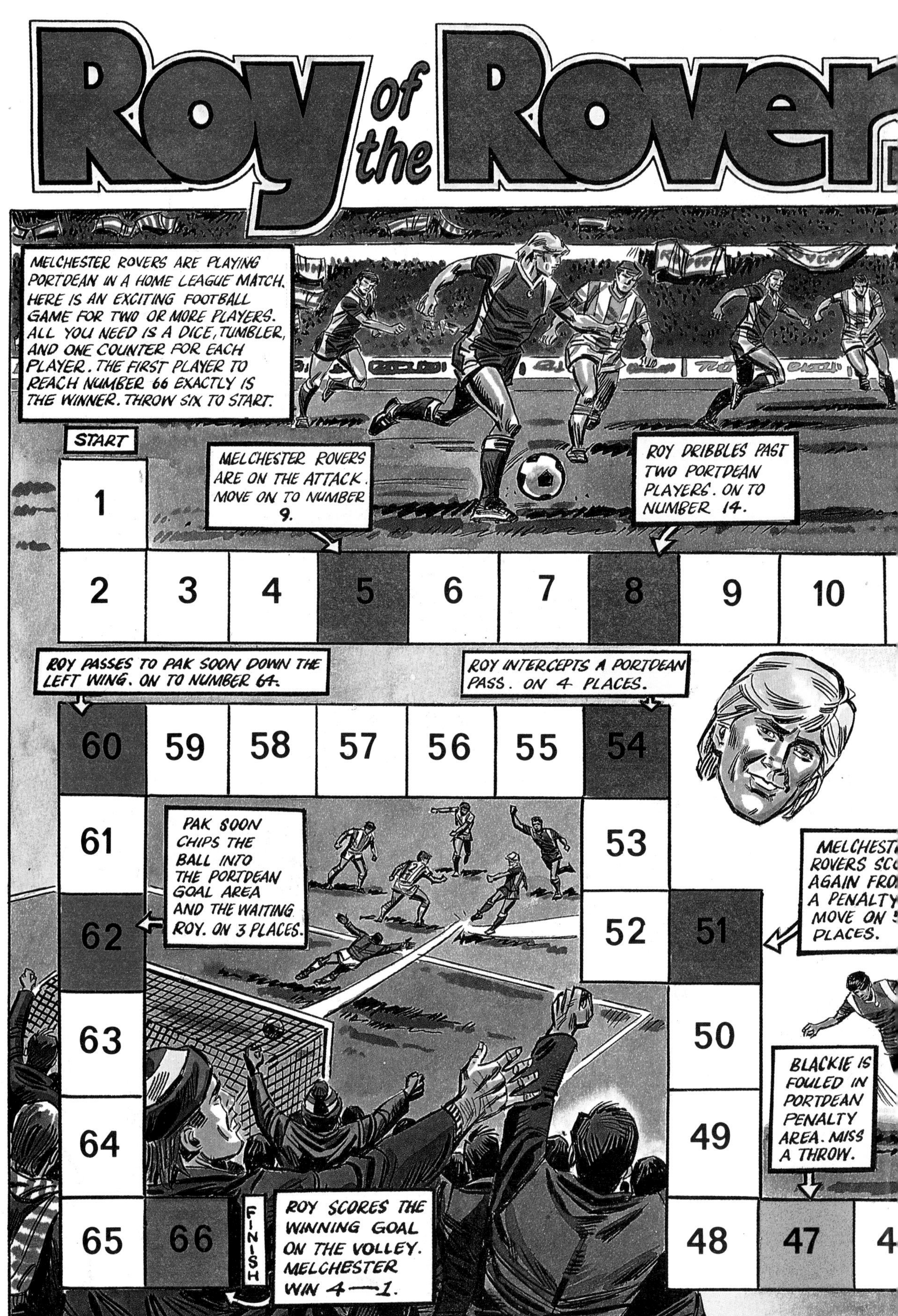
Roy of the
MELCHESTER ROVERS ARE PLAYING PORTDEAN IN A HOME LEAGUE MATCH. HERE IS AN EXCITING FOOTBALL GAME FOR TWO OR MORE PLAYERS. ALL YOU NEED IS A DICE, TUMBLER, AND ONE COUNTER FOR EACH PLAYER. THE FIRST PLAYER TO REACH NUMBER 66 EXACTLY IS THE WINNER. THROW SIX TO START.
START
1
MELCHESTER ROVERS ARE ON THE ATTACK. MOVE ON TO NUMBER 9.
ROY DRIBBLES PAST TWO PORTDEAN PLAYERS. ON TO NUMBER 14.
2 3 4 5 6 7 8 9 10
ROY PASSES TO PAK SOON DOWN THE LEFT WING. ON TO NUMBER 64.
ROY INTERCEPTS A PORTDEAN PASS. ON 4 PLACES.
60 59 58 57 56 55 54
61
PAK SOON CHIPS THE BALL INTO THE PORTDEAN GOAL AREA AND THE WAITING ROY. ON 3 PLACES.
53
62
52 51
63
50
BLACKIE IS FOULED IN PORTDEAN PENALTY AREA. MISS A THROW.
64
49
65 66
FINISH
ROY SCORES THE WINNING GOAL ON THE VOLLEY. MELCHESTER WIN 4—1.
48 47